L-Plate
Vegan

the pocket guide to
animal-free shopping

The L-Plate Vegan © Viva!
Viva!, 8 York Court, Wilder Street, Bristol BS2 8QH
www.viva.org.uk
info@viva.org.uk
T 0117 944 1000

Vegan and Proud!

Viva!

Now be loud! Join Viva! and save animals. Your donation will help us to continue sending undercover teams into factory farms and slaughterhouses to expose the misery of factory farming. Our campaigns save animals and bring about change – which is why meat consumption is falling.

Join us for only £15 (£12 unwaged) a year and receive

- *Viva!Life* magazine 3 times a year, full colour and includes features, competitions, recipes and more
- free car sticker
- Supporter's Card, saving you £££s at hundreds of shops, holidays and restaurants in the UK and abroad

☐ **I want to join Viva!**

Title _____ First name _____

Surname _____

Address _____

_____ Postcode _____

Tel _____

Email _____

Send a cheque payable to Viva! to:
Viva!, 8 York Court, Wilder St, Bristol BS2 8QH
Call 0117 944 1000 or join online www.viva.org.uk

Viva!

LPV

Whether you are…

- a new vegan
- vegan-curious
- trying to reduce dairy and eggs
- a seasoned vegan in search of instant meals

This guide will help you find an animal-free alternative wherever you are!

Being vegan has never been easier. Even tiny convenience stores now stock vegan sausages and soya milk. And statistics show a huge rise in the sales of meat-free and free-from products, with over 35 million people in the UK eating vegetarian/vegan more of the time. Mintel – the prestigious survey company – predicts that meat-free and free-from food sales will top £1 billion in 2013. Vegans are an important part of that market.

Veganism is a positive step – you will discover a big new world of exciting food, rather than 'giving up' animal products. It's much easier than you think – and not only are you helping to save animals and the environment but it's good for your health too. Result!

Explore vegan recipes of every type, from cakes to cookies, 'cheese' to 'chicken' and gorgeous ways with veggies! Whether you are a novice or an experienced cook, you will find plenty of inspiration on www.veganrecipeclub.org.uk – Viva!'s celebrated recipe site. With over 500 recipes (and growing), articles, nutritional information, a blog and dedicated Facebook page… it's got the lot.

Disclaimer: This information is accurate to the best of our ability but Viva! cannot be held responsible for inaccurate labelling or for companies 'de-veganising' their products.

Viva!

Contents

FOX HALL VEGAN B&B

@ Prizet Stables,
Helsington, Kendal
Cumbria, LA8 8AB

Tel. Sylvia or Chris on
015395 61241
Email: fox.hall@btinternet.com
Website: www.fox.hall.btinternet.co.uk

We are 2 miles south of Kendal, South Lakes, 10 mins by car from M6 junction 36, 20 mins from Windermere on the A591 & 10 mins from Oxenholme railway station.

- ✓ *4 Guest Rooms, all en-suite*
- ✓ *Children very welcome*
- ✓ *Special Diets catered for*
- ✓ *Evening Meals available*
- ✓ *Organic food*
- ✓ *Vegan Cookery Courses*

Our nearest tourist attractions are Levens Hall & Sizergh Castle. There are good local walks along the Lancaster to Kendal Canal towpath, River Kent and into Levens Park as well as Scout Scar & The Helm.

Registered by the Vegan Society

"A no-smoking, eco-friendly family home with organic food where children are always welcome"

Please visit our website for more up-to-date information on accommodation, availability, location, menus, cookery courses and much more!

What is a vegan, anyway?

- Someone who eats a huge range of delicious food!
- Someone who doesn't eat, wear or use anything that comes from any animal, dead or alive.

That means 'no thanks' to:

- meat (beef, lamb, pork, goat etc) – or anything from them (pâté, bacon, brawn etc)
- poultry (chicken, turkey, duck, goose, pheasant etc) – or anything from them (chicken liver; foie gras etc)
- fish or fish roe (caviar etc)
- water creatures, sea or fresh-water (prawns, oysters, crabs, lobsters, mussels etc)
- by-products from animals such as gelatine, animal fat (lard), isinglass (fish bladders), lanolin (sheep's wool – often from slaughtered sheep)
- dairy (milk, cheese, cream, yoghurt, crème fraiche etc)
- eggs
- by-products from dairy or eggs such as whey, skimmed milk, casein, albumen
- honey – because bees are frequently killed during its production. And it's their food, not ours!
- leather, wool or silk – a lot of wool comes from slaughtered sheep. Leather and silk involve death for creatures
- cosmetics or toiletries that contain animal substances

And see page 94-96 for a more comprehensive list!

Viva!

Why vegan?
Four good reasons

1. It's good for you

Science is on our side! All major health organisations from the World Health Organisation (WHO) to the British Medical Association (BMA) and the American Dietetic Association (ADA) agree that a vegan diet reduces the risk of:

- heart disease
- high blood pressure
- stroke
- diabetes type two
- some cancers – especially breast, prostate, colorectal
- rheumatoid arthritis
- kidney stones
- asthma
- allergies

It also reduces the chance of you contracting food poisoning to almost zero. And of course you avoid all those chemicals and antibiotics that are pumped into animals.

For further information see:
Viva! Guide 7 – Your Health in Your Hands
www.viva.org.uk/yourhealth

Viva! Guide 2 – Stop Bugging Me
www.viva.org.uk/stopbuggingme

L-Plate Vegan

2. It's good for the animals

If you're already a vegetarian you've undoubtedly helped reduce animal suffering, but the dairy industry is strongly linked to the meat industry. Also, egg-laying hens are killed at 18 months to two years for 'low-grade' meat. Here are some more reasons:

- Cows must be repeatedly made pregnant for the production of milk.
  - Their babies are either killed at one or two days old or reared for veal, beef or milk.
  - Dairy cows are killed between four-five years because they are too worn out to produce enough milk for the industry's demands. Naturally, they would live until at least 20.
  - Each year some 150,000 dairy cows are still pregnant when killed in the UK.
- Goats kept for milk are also killed prematurely for goat meat – often by religious slaughter methods for an ethnic trade.
- Sheep – the males are slaughtered when very young and their bodies sold as lamb; the females are slaughtered when they become too weak to bear more lambs.
- Chickens (and ducks, geese etc)
  - Caged egg production: hens are imprisoned in cages, row upon row.
  - Since only the females lay eggs, up to 40 million day-old male chicks are killed every year in the UK alone.
  - Free range, barn eggs and other such welfare labels are no guarantee that eggs are cruelty-free – large scale commercial production can mean thousands of hens on the floor of a shed never finding their way outdoors.
  - RSPCA's Freedom Food symbol approves factory farms so is no guarantee that hens are genuinely free range.
  - Whether battery, free range or organic, all laying hens are killed prematurely when they are too worn out to lay enough eggs for the industry. Their bodies are made into

stock cubes, soups, baby food or pies.
- Eggs marked 'free range' and 'Approved by the Soil Association' does mean that animal welfare standards are higher than the norm (but the male chicks are still killed).

For further information see:
Viva! Guide 11 – A Matter of Life and Death.
www.viva.org.uk/guides/animals

3. It's good for the environment
Cycling to work is good but a vegan diet is miles better.

- Meat and dairy produce more greenhouse gases than all the world's transport put together. The billions of cows and other animals which humans breed for profit produce massive quantities of gas – farts and belches, in other words! This gas is actually nitrous oxide and methane, which contributes hugely to global warming.
- Forests across the world are destroyed to farm or grow feed for farmed animals and so are British woods and hedgerows. This is the number one cause of loss of wildlife species worldwide.
- We could produce far more plant foods to feed humans in the UK instead of using most of it to feed animals.
- In addition, the soil is poisoned with chemicals to increase crop production that is destined for animal feed.
- Organic or not, animals poo and wee in mighty quantities. As a result our waterways are polluted with livestock slurry.

For further information see:
Viva! Guide 9 – Planet on a Plate
www.vivashop.org.uk/books/planet-plate-guide and
www.viva.org.uk/hot

4. It's good for the planet's people.

- 800 million people are hungry and there's no need!
- We could easily produce enough food to feed everyone if only we stopped feeding all the crops to the animals.
- Richer countries are eating more and more meat. This, plus recent crop failures, means that global food shortages are predicted to get even worse: more people will starve across the world.
- 100kg of plant protein produces only 9kg of beef protein or 31kg of milk protein. Doesn't it make sense to just eat the plants?!

For further information see:
Viva! Guide 12 – Feed the World.
www.vivashop.org.uk/books/feed-world-guide

Viva!

High street top 20 products and Quick Fix Meal ideas

While Viva! does its best to promote independents, the reality is that many towns and cities in the UK have lost many of their small businesses. Supermarkets are major players who have taken over most of the UK's food production and distribution.

www.tescopoly.org offers an alternative point of view. Also, you may start to find out more about food manufacturers – eg some vegan products are manufactured by non-vegan companies who are unethical in other areas. But don't feel you need to do everything at once! Start off simply, have fun and don't worry – any fine-tuning you want to do can come later.

In the meantime, supermarkets do offer an increasingly wide range of vegan food…

- We list each supermarket's own brand where possible but, of course, they sell vegan products from other companies.
- Aldi, Lidl, Netto or Spar are not included, mainly because they hold smaller stock lines and/or lack a vegan list. However, these shops often sell quality products at bargain prices – Lidl's nuts and wraps spring to mind!
- Larger supermarket branches sell a wider range of vegan products – a small local store may not sell everything listed here.
- Free-from and ethnic sections are good places to start looking as well as the more obvious vegetarian and wholefood areas.
- Most of the major supermarkets offer a vegan list online or by email, which is updated regularly (we've given a link where possible).

- Companies may delete or replace products and brands without warning so don't blame us if they no longer sell a product!
- When in doubt, always read the packet – or ask in-store customer services.

What we DON'T list (instrincally vegan products):

- cooking oils. Rapeseed, olive, ground nut, sesame, sunflower or plain
- fresh vegetables and fresh fruit. Most tinned varieties are vegan, as are the frozen varieties
- jam and marmalade
- nuts and seeds
- nut and seed butters (peanut, cashew, almond, pumpkin seed, tahini etc)
- pasta/noodles. These are usually vegan but watch out for egg in fresh varieties or some dried such as tagliatelle or egg noodles
- plant milks, eg soya, nut, oat, rice
- pulses – beans, peas and lentils. Buy them dried, tinned, frozen or in pouches without other ingredients added
- rice and other grains – unless they are part of a dish or packet with other ingredients
- soya sauce. Tamari is wheat/gluten-free, shoyu isn't, but both are kitchen wizards
- tea and coffee. Basic types don't add anything dodgy. A tiny handful of herb teas may have added honey; hot chocolate may have added dairy (whey or milk powder). Cocoa is always vegan.

Vegan or allergen-free?

If an item has no animal ingredients in it but the packaging states may contain traces of milk/egg... this means the item is most likely vegan.

Companies who make a variety of foods have to clean the production lines between different batches, eg foods containing nuts, soya, dairy etc. For example, a chocolate manufacturer may make a batch of non-vegan milk chocolate then clean the line and make a batch of vegan dark chocolate!

Although the lines are cleaned scrupulously, there is always the risk of microscopic traces and companies have a legal obligation to warn allergy sufferers about possible cross contamination. From an ethical point of view, most vegan groups agree that this is an acceptable compromise. While it is undoubtedly better to support dedicated vegan companies, it isn't always practical. Being able to buy items from mainstream companies widens the choice of products available to vegans. As ever, when in doubt, check with the manufacturer.

For further information see the Vegan Society's useful article. www.vegansociety.com/about/policies/allergy-labelling.aspx

Top 20

We have chosen our top 20 vegan items from each supermarket – obviously they sell much more! We've also given you quick meal ideas for each supermarket.

Asda top 20

www.asda.com T: 0800 952 6060
A list for summer 2012 was spotted on a vegan website **www.c-a-l-f.com/easy-vegan** – yet a nice (and vegan!) Asda customer services person told us the company had stopped compiling a vegan list. We chose the following vegan items:

1. Asda Vegetarian Spicy Bean & Nacho Burgers
2. Asda Vegetarian Falafels
3. Asda Vegetable Hotpot
4. Asda Vegetable Goulash Crispbakes
5. Asda Lemon & Herb Piri Piri Quarter Pounders
6. Asda Chicken-style Pieces
7. Asda Vegetarian Mince
8. Asda Meat-free dried mixes: Mexican Chilli; Sausage; Falafel; Lincolnshire Sausage. Cheap and handy! Replace egg in packet instructions with 1-2 tbsp sieved gram flour mixed to a smooth paste with a little water
9. Asda Patatas Bravas
10. Asda Cous Cous Harissa Chickpea Salad
11. Asda Edamame Bean Salad
12. Asda White Bean & Pepper Hummus (plus many others in the hummus range)
13. Asda Fresh Soups: Chunky Vegetable Goulash; Extra Special Miso & Vegetable Soup; Good For You Roasted Red Pepper & Haricot Bean Soup; Good For You Spicy Lentil & Vegetable Soup

14. Asda Eco-Friendly Double Concentrated Liquid Wash – the website declares that it's vegan. Sadly, other products in the range are not defined as such.
15. Linda McCartney: Sausage Rolls; Sausages; Country Pie; Mushroom & Ale Pie; Veggie Mince
16. Innocent Veg Pots – most are vegan bar one or two – check the label
17. Free From Chocolate Bar
18. Choices, Caramel-flavoured
19. Goody Good sweets (but check, as some of their range contains beeswax)
20. Tofu
    - Plain – Cauldron Firm
    - Pieces, Marinated – Cauldron
    - Silken – Mori-nu

Asda Quick Fix Meal 1. Mexican-style. 7-10 minutes

Asda Vegetarian Spicy Bean & Nacho Burgers and Asda Patatas Bravas. Microwave these according to packet instructions. Serve with a dollop of Alpro plain vegan yoghurt plus a green salad with avocado.

Asda Quick Fix Meal 2. Italian-style. 10-15 minutes

Asda Rigatoni pasta – cook enough for your meal. Meanwhile, fry half a red onion with crushed garlic – cook for 2-3 minutes, add ½-1 pack of Asda Mixed Pepper Stir-Fry. Stir in some Asda Chicken-style Pieces and sauté everything for another 2-3 minutes. Finally, stir in a pasta sauce such as Asda Chosen by You Tomato & Olive Stir-In Pasta Sauce or Loyd Grossman Tomato & Basil. Drain the pasta, mix it into the sauce and serve hot.

Asda Quick Fix Meal 3. Middle Eastern-style. 5 minutes

Asda Vegetarian Falafels – warmed through for a minute or two in the microwave. Toast some pitta bread. Serve the falafels and pitta with Asda White Bean & Pepper Hummus and Asda Edamame Bean Salad – plus instant tomato salad: slice up a tomato, chop a few leaves of fresh basil and sprinkle on top. Add a drizzle of olive oil and salt.

Co-op

www.co-operativefood.co.uk T: 0800 0686 727

The Co-op's own-brand labelling system makes vegan shopping easier. As well as food, their own-brand booze includes many vegan-friendly wines, beers and ciders and they also do a small cruelty-free range of toiletries and cleaning products. They will also send a vegan list if you contact them. However, their range of vegan products overall is more limited than the other major supermarkets, partly because they tend to have smaller branches.

1. Co-op Onion Bhajis
2. Co-op Takeaway Bombay Potatoes
3. Co-op Takeaway Pilau Rice
4. Co-op Indian snacks
5. Co-op Hummus (not Moroccan)
6. Co-op Frozen Onion Rings
7. Co-op Doughnuts: Jam; Custard
8. Co-op Fruit Pies: Apple; Cherry
9. Co-op Frozen: Raspberries; Summer Fruits
10. Co-op Fresh Soups: Garden Vegetable Soup with Barley; Limited Edition Summer Vegetable Broth; Limited Edition Winter Root Vegetable & Lentil Soup; Pea & Mint Soup; Limited Edition Moroccan Spiced Chickpea Soup; Three Bean & Italian Tomato Soup; Tomato & Chilli Soup; Tomato & Lentil Soup

11. Co-op Christmas Puddings: Rich Fruit Christmas Pudding; Truly Irresistible Christmas Pudding
12. Co-op Gravy Granules: Gravy Granules; Gravy Granules For Meat
13. Co-op Peruvian Dark Chocolate with Dried Sweetened Cranberries
14. Co-op Tinned Pulses – assorted
15. Co-op Chocolate Cake Mix – see page 66
16. Tofu: Cauldron Plain Firm
17. Margarine: Pure
18. Linda McCartney Country Pies
19. Thai Taste Thai curry pack
20. Innocent Veg Pots – most are vegan but check the label

Co-op Quick Fix Meal 1. Italian-style. 10 minutes

Co-op Truly Irresistible Pennoni Rigate cooked and drained. Stir in Co-op Truly Irresistible Sun-Dried Tomato and Basil Pasta Sauce, tinned kidney beans and chopped olives. Serve with rocket salad and balsamic dressing.

Co-op Quick Fix Meal 2. Indian-style. 10-15 minutes

Starter: Co-op Onion Bhajis served with mango chutney – warm through in oven or microwave
Main: Microwave Co-op Takeaway Bombay Potatoes served with Co-op Takeaway Pilau Rice. Make a second curry by mixing 1 tin of chickpeas with a jar of Co-op Healthy Living Jalfrezi Cooking Sauce and a large handful of fresh baby spinach – cook for about 2-3 minutes on the stove. If desired, add steamed vegetables from the Co-op mixed vegetable pack.

L-Plate
Vegan

Co-op Quick Fix Meal 3. Pie and Mash.
30 minutes

Pre-heat the oven. Prepare the potatoes and boil with a little salt.
Bake Linda McCartney Country Pies in the oven. Prepare any
vegetables you want – steam or microwave. Make Bisto gravy.
Drain the potatoes then mash with soya milk and Pure margarine.
Serve the pie, vegetables, mash and gravy hot.

Viva!

Holland & Barrett

www.hollandandbarrett.com

T: 0870 606 6605 (this is for H&B's mail order service – there is no central number for store queries. Alternatively, phone your local branch.)

Many H&B sell a good range of foods while some have ditched their frozen and/or chilled range, so check your local branch!

1. Amy's: Bean & Rice Burrito; Indian Vegetable Korma; Black Bean Enchilada
2. Fry's: Hot dogs
3. Fry's: Chunky Strips
4. Fry's: Breaded Schnitzels
5. Fry's: Sausages
6. Fry's: Burgers – Chicken-style and Traditional
7. Fry's: Chicken-style Nuggets
8. Fry's: Poloni
9. Fry's: Pies – Country Mushroom and Pepper Steak-style
10. Garden Lites: Courgette Portabello
11. Mama Cucina: Vegetable Pizza; Vegetable Quiches; Cheesecake
12. Real Eat: Chicken-style Pieces
13. Redwood Pizzas – Cheezly & Tomato; Meatless Feast. Pork-style Sausage Rolls; Meatless Meatballs
14. Swedish Glace Ice Cream: assorted flavours
15. Vegetarian Choice: Lincolnshire Sausages
16. Alpro yoghurt: assorted flavours
17. Redwood: Cheatin Slices, assorted, eg Chicken-style; Redwood Cheezly: assorted flavours including Soya-Free; Redwood Roasts, assorted
18. Holland & Barrett: Vegetarian Jumbo Sos Roll; H&B Porkless Pie
19. VegOut pastry slices: Steakless Bake; No Chorizo & Mexican Bean
20. Free & Easy: Dairy-free Cheese Flavour Mix

L-Plate Vegan

H&B Quick Fix Meal 1. Vegan Caesar-style Salad. 10 minutes

Fry half a pack of Fry's Chunky Strips. Mix a couple of tablespoons of Plamil or other vegan mayo with a little soya or rice milk to thin down. Add the strips and mayo to a large green salad and mix everything well. Top with croutons and toasted seeds. Serve with crusty bread.

H&B Quick Fix Meal 2. USA All-day Breakfast. 20 minutes

Cook Fry's Hot Dogs in a little oil for a few minutes – and steam some broccoli or other vegetables of your choice. And perhaps some baked beans and toast! McCain's Hash Browns are another American-style addition – not sold by H&B however. Serve everything hot with tomato ketchup on the side.

H&B Quick Fix Meal 3. Quiche-style. 30 minutes (mostly baking time)

Mama Cucina Quiche served with Garden Lites' Courgette Portabello and steamed green veggies or a green salad.

21

Marks & Spencer

www.marksandspencer.com T: 0845 609 0200
They provide a vegan list which is regularly updated
www.health.marksandspencer.com/uploads/pdfs/vegan.pdf
M&S is great for lunches/snacks – their mixed salads in particular
are excellent, but watch for feta/yoghurt/honey in dressings!
Many of their vegetarian main meals are unsuitable for vegans
but they do sell a lot of vegan-friendly booze.

1. M&S Cauliflower & Chickpea Curry
2. M&S Spiced Red Lentil Kofte with Tabbouleh
3. M&S Tuscan Bean, Pasta & Vegetable Stew
4. M&S Braised Vegetable Casserole with Mini Parsley
    Dumplings
5. M&S Ratatouille
6. M&S Valencia Vegetable Paella
7. M&S Meat Free Soya Mince
8. M&S Mediterranean Vegetable Pasta with Red Pepper Sauce
9. M&S Mexican Bean & Butternut Chilli Snackpot
10. M&S Smoothies: Passion Fruit; Super Berry
11. M&S Jellies: Raspberry; Mojito; Peach Melba; Fresh Fruit;
    Pina Colada; Pomegranate & Elderflower; 3 Mini Retro Jellies
    (multipack)
12. M&S Margarine: Sunflower Spread; Sunflower Spread Light
    Dairy-free
13. M&S Salads: Asian Slaw & Mango Rice Salad with Edamame
    Bean Dip; Orzo Pasta Dual Tray; Orzo Pasta with Slow
    Roasted Tomatoes; Cous Cous with Roasted Butternut
    Squash; Superwholefood Shaker Salad
14. M&S Large Deli Salads: Roasted Vegetable Cous Cous; Rice
    Lentil & Aubergine; Edamame Bean
15. M&S Hummus, assorted flavours; Reduced-fat with Carrot
    Batons (one portion)
16. M&S Fresh soups: Tomato & Basil; Super Green; Summer

Minestrone; Super Beetroot

17. M&S Wraps: Red Pepper Hummus Wrap; Sweet Chilli Vegetable Sushi Wrap
18. M&S Lemon Sorbet (freezer)
19. M&S Vegetable Spring Rolls; Oriental Vegetable Selection (freezer)
20. M&S Green Thai Curry Cooking Sauce

M&S Quick Fix Meal 1. Gourmet Salad Platter. 5 minutes

M&S Large Deli Salad – Roasted Vegetable Cous Cous plus M&S Large Deli Salad – Edamame Bean. Serve with M&S Super Green Bowl Salad plus M&S Chilli & Coriander Dressing. M&S Peach Melba Jelly Dessert (sold in a pot) for pudding!

M&S Quick Fix Meal 2. Winter Warmer. 20 minutes

M&S Braised Vegetable Casserole with Mini Parsley Dumplings, served with oven-baked M&S Maris Piper Onion Rosti and one of their prepared green vegetable selection, steamed or microwaved.

M&S Quick Fix Meal 3. Mediterranean-style. 10 minutes

M&S Ratatouille with added chickpeas or kidney beans. Serve with M&S Cous Cous with Roasted Butternut Squash plus steamed/microwaved spinach or broccoli.

Morrisons

www.morrisons.co.uk T: 0845 611 6111

Sadly, Morrisons has no vegan list but hopefully this will change soon!

1. Morrisons Antipasti range in jars: Roasted Red Peppers; Mixed Chilli Peppers; Chargrilled Artichokes; Chargrilled Aubergines; Sun-dried Tomatoes; Mixed Mushrooms; Olives – assorted; Sliced Jalapeno Chillies
2. Morrisons Wholefoods Ready to Eat: Spelt, Lentils & Brown Rice; Quinoa, Cereals & Kidney beans; Puy Lentils
3. Morrisons Pulses, good range of tinned, eg Black-eyed Peas; Borlotti Beans; Chickpeas; Whole Lentils – plus Mixed (unflavoured) Beans: Indian Salad mix; Oriental Salad mix; Mexican Salad mix. Also Curried
4. Morrisons chilled snacks: Mini Indian Selection; Vegetable Samosas; Vegetable Spring Rolls
5. Morrisons chilled Dahl & Roasted Vegetables
6. Morrisons frozen: Butternut Squash & Nut Roasts; Vegetable & Tomato Bakes
7. Morrisons Meat Free: Chicken-style Pieces; Veggie Mince (Rest of range not vegan)
8. Morrisons Wholefood Salads: Giant Couscous & Chinese Edamame; Roasted Beetroot, Bulgur & Braeburn Apple
9. Morrisons Pastry, fresh and frozen: Puff or Shortcrust
10. Morrisons Savers biscuits: Bourbon; Digestives; Ginger; Fruit Shortbread; Rich Tea
11. Morrisons breakfast cereals: Wholewheat Muesli; Cranberry Wheats; Blueberry Wheats; Savers Bran Flakes
12. Morrisons Finely Chopped Tomatoes in cartons: Chilli; Herb; Olive Oil; Roasted Garlic & Onion; Plain
13. Linda McCartney Sausages; Country Pies
14. Tofu: Cauldron Plain Firm
15. Margarine: Pure and Vitalite

16. Swedish Glace, vanilla
17. Alpro Soya Desserts, assorted flavours; Alpro custard
18. Discovery: Fajita kit; Enchilada kit. Others items in the range are vegan but check labels
19. Loyd Grossman: Balti Sauce (many of the Italian range too but check labels)
20. Seeds of Change: Organic Classic Bolognese; Organic Tomato & Basil

Morrisons Quick Fix Meal 1. Italian Antipasti Salad Platter. 10 minutes

One bowl of Morrisons Mixed Leaf Salad with added cherry tomatoes, grated carrot and cucumber. One bowl of microwaved Morrisons Wholefoods Ready to Eat Quinoa mixed in with Morrisons Wholefoods Ready to Eat Puy Lentils. Top with a handful each of Morrisons Chargrilled Artichokes and Morrisons Chargrilled Aubergines – or roasted red peppers and olives. Serve with wholemeal pitta and a little hummus if desired.

Viva!

Morrisons Quick Fix Meal 2. Roast Dinner. 20-30 minutes

Morrisons Butternut Squash & Nut Roasts; serve with home-cooked mashed potatoes; steamed broccoli or other veg*; Bisto (red tub) gravy.

*Many microwaveable ready-to-eat veg contain butter, cream or other non-vegan ingredients.

Morrisons Quick Fix Meal 3. Mexican-style. 15-20 minutes

Discovery Enchilada Kit. Gently fry half a pack of Morrisons Stir-fry Mix with peppers. Add 100g/generous 3oz of Morrisons Veggie Mince or Morrisons Chicken-style Pieces plus half a tin of kidney or pinto beans and cook for a few minutes along with the packet of spices from the kit, stirring occasionally. Add the sauce from the kit and mix everything well. Let it cook for about 5 minutes on a low heat, stirring occasionally. Meanwhile, steam lots of green veggies – broccoli, cabbage etc – or else make a green leaf and avocado salad. Warm through the corn tortillas in the enchilada kit and serve with the rest of the meal.

Sainsbury's

www.sainsburys.co.uk T: 0800 636 262

They have a vegan list which is updated regularly.

www2.sainsburys.co.uk/food/allergies-intolerances/product-guides/product_guides.htm

Sainsbury's has a good range of vegan foods and is increasingly labelling its own brands, though not always consistently. Many of their own-brand wines are labelled vegan.

1. Sainsbury's Butternut Squash & Moroccan-style Cous Cous
2. Sainsbury's Indian Baby Corn & Pepper Masala
3. Sainsbury's Channa Masala
4. Sainsbury's Indian Vegetable Jalfrezi
5. Sainsbury's Mini Onion Bhajis
6. Sainsbury's Vegetable & Bean Chilli
7. Sainsbury's Red Tomato Rice
8. Sainsbury's Mixed Olive Antipasti
9. Sainsbury's Free-from Spread (margarine)
10. Sainsbury's Thin & Crispy Pizza Bases – and Sainsbury's Pizza Sauce Topping
11. Sainsbury's Salad Pots including: Beetroot; Tomato & Basil Pasta; Jewelled Cous Cous; Carrot & Poppy Seed; Four Bean; Roasted Vegetable Couscous; Chargrilled Vegetable Pasta; Tomato & Jalapeño Pepper Pasta; Bulghur Wheat & Carrot
12. Sainsbury's Salad Dressings: Organic French Dressing; French Dressing; Be Good To Yourself Vinaigrette (low-fat); Balsamic; Mango, Lime & Chilli
13. Sainsbury's Meat-free: Nut Cutlets; Spicy Bean Quarter Pounders; Basics Vegetable Sausages; Meat-free Sausage Rolls; Meat-free Sausages; Moroccan-style Burgers; Vegetable Quarter Pounders
14. Sainsbury's Instant Noodle or Pasta Pots: Chicken Noodles; Vegetable Flavour; Chicken Curry Flavour; Instant Noodles Chicken Flavour; Basics Chicken Curry Flavour; Basics Pasta

Shells in a Tomato & Onion Sauce Mix
15. Sainsbury's Cranberry, Orange & Port Sauce
16. Sainsbury's Dips: Be Good To Yourself Reduced-fat Guacamole; Chunky Salsa Dip; SO Organic Houmous; Be Good To Yourself Reduced-fat Mini Houmous Snack Pots and regular tub; Caramelised Onion Houmous; Basic Houmous; Piri Piri Houmous; Sweet Harissa Houmous; Topped Supreme Houmous; Topped Cannellini Bean Houmous; Roasted Carrot & Coriander Houmous; Pea & Mint Houmous
17. Sainsbury's Pastry: Puff Pastry Block 500 gram; Puff Pastry Ready Rolled; Lighter Shortcrust Pastry Ready Rolled; Shortcrust Pastry Ready Rolled; Filo
18. Sainsbury's Biscuits: Oaty; Digestives; Be Good To Yourself Reduced-fat Ginger Snaps; Cranberry Oaty Mini; Chocolate Oaty Mini; Basics Ginger Snaps; Ginger Snaps; Morning Coffee
19. Sainsbury's Jelly Desserts: Mandarin; Raspberry
20. Sainsbury's Belgian Cooking Chocolate, Plain – good value and at 50% cocoa solids nice enough to eat on its own!

Sainsbury's Quick Fix Meal 1. Pizza with Houmous or Vegan Cheese. 10 minutes

Pre-heat oven according to pizza base packet instructions. Spread Sainsbury's Pizza Sauce on a Sainsbury's Thin & Crispy Pizza Base. Add sliced mushrooms plus Sainsbury's Pitted Natural Black Olives and Sainsbury's Chargrilled Red Peppers. Dot some Sainsbury's Houmous over the vegetables (regular or cannellini bean flavour).* Bake in the oven for 10 minutes or until the base is properly cooked. Serve with Sainsbury's Italian-style Salad mixed with Sainsbury's Watercress.

*Alternatively, grate melting vegan cheese such as Redwood Melting Mozzarella – not available from Sainsbury's at time of writing.

MAKE YOUR NEXT STOP VIVA!'S CHOCOLATE SHOP

Gooey n' Chewy 'Milk' Chocolate
Snack-size bars crammed with roasted nuts, toasted coconut and vanilla caramel.

Dreamy n' Creamy White Chocolate
Dairy-free squares of white chocolate topped with strawberries, raspberries, coconut and sugar rice crisps.

Crunchy n' Munchy Dark Chocolate Snacks
Tiny morsels of toasted soya beans and pumpkin seeds covered in organic dark chocolate.

Viva!

GET YOUR CHOCOLATE FIX AT VIVA!'S DEDICATED VEGAN SHOP
WWW.VIVASHOP.ORG.UK
ORDER ONLINE OR CALL 0117 944 1000 (MON-FRI, 9AM-6PM)

Viva!

Sainsbury's Quick Fix Meal 2. Thai-style. 15 minutes

Put rice on to cook according to packet instructions. Dry rice takes 11 minutes. (If using another type, eg Sainsbury's White Rice Microwavable Bags, check packet instructions.) Meanwhile, sauté a pack of Sainsbury's Taste the Difference Aromatic Stir-fry Vegetables. Mix in Thai Taste Green Curry Meal Kit (includes coconut milk). Simmer gently until the vegetables are just tender. Mix in a pack of Cauldron Marinated Tofu Pieces and serve the curry with the cooked, drained rice.

Sainsbury's Quick Fix Meal 3. Chinese-style. 7-10 minutes

Cook Sainsbury's Rice Noodles (fresh) according to packet instructions. Meanwhile, lightly fry a pack of Sainsbury's Basics Stir-fry Vegetables. Stir in Sainsbury's Hoisin & Garlic Stir-fry Sauce and a pack of Cauldron Marinated Tofu Pieces and/or a few handfuls of frozen peas.

Tesco

www.tesco.com T: 08457 22 55 33

Tesco has a vegan list which is updated regularly
http://realfood.tesco.com/healthy-eating/vegetarian-and-vegan-diets.html

It also sells a substantial free-from and meat-free range, some of which is suitable for vegans. Its free-from dairy range includes soft and hard vegan cheese and yoghurt. Some of its ethnic chilled and frozen meals are also suitable for vegans.

1. Tesco Free-from Cheese Alternative Spread: Soya Mild; Soya Medium
2. Tesco Free-from Cheese Alternative, Creamy Original; Creamy Cheddar; Creamy Garlic & Herb; Creamy Sweet Chilli
3. Tesco Free-from margarine: Free-from Soya Spread; Free-from Sunflower Spread
4. Cream Alternatives: Alpro (long life or fresh)
5. Tesco Free-from Milk Alternatives: Soya (fresh, long life, sweetened, unsweetened); Rice; Coconut; Coconut & Chocolate Milk; Hazelnut; Chocolate Shakes
6. Tesco Natural Alternative to Yoghurt: Cherry; Mango; Passion Fruit; Mixed Berries
7. Tesco Toi Mushroom & Pea Masala
8. Tesco Toi Gobi Aloo
9. Tesco Pilau Rice
10. Tesco Mini Indian Selection
11. Tesco Free-from Desserts: Chocolate; Vanilla; Crème Caramel
12. Pastry: Tesco Ready Rolled Shortcrust; Ready Rolled Puff; Ready Rolled Light Shortcrust; Ready Rolled Light Puff
13. Tesco Trattoria Verdi Gnocchi
14. Tesco Wholegrain Microwave Rice – brown rice in a ping!
15. Tesco Meat-free Range: Value Vegetable Burger; Falafels; Mexican Style Salsa Bake; Curry Bakes; Vegetable Quarter Pounders; Vegetable Fingers; Nut Cutlets; Mexican Style Bean Burgers; Meat-free Mince; Chickpea & Barley Gumbo

16. Tesco Vegetable Spring Rolls
17. Tesco Houmous & Carrot Chutney Sandwich
18. Tesco Gravy: Vegetable Stockpot; Oak Lane Vegetable Gravy Granules; Onion Gravy Granules; Reduced Salt Gravy Granules; Vegetable Gravy Granules
19. Tesco Casserole Packet Sauces: Spanish Chicken Recipe Mix; One Pot Slow Cooked Beef Seasoning; Garlic & Herb Chicken Recipe Mix; Hunters Chicken Sauce; Sundried Tomato & Cinnamon Sauce (these don't contain meat, despite their names! Try them in vegan casseroles, replacing the meat with tofu, beans or vegan 'chicken' pieces)
20. Tesco Thai Curry Pastes: Yellow; Green; Red

Tesco Quick Fix Meal 1. Italian-style. 5-10 minutes

Tesco Trattoria Verdi Gnocchi topped with Tesco Chargrilled Vegetable Sauce (add half a tin of Tesco Cannellini or Tesco Haricot Beans for protein). Served with Tesco Rainbow Stir-fry.

Tesco Quick Fix Meal 2. Chinese-style. 10 minutes

Tesco Vegetable & Beansprout Stir-fry cooked in a wok or deep frying pan with Tesco Soya Beans (frozen). Heat Tesco Ken Hom Hot & Spicy Kung Po Cooking Sauce and mix in with the stir-fry and soya beans. Serve with Tesco Rice Noodles (fresh). If you don't like spicy food, try Tesco Sticky Plum & Hoi Sin Stir-fry Sauce or similar.

Tesco Quick Fix Meal 3. Mexican-style. 30 minutes

Tesco Mexican Style Salsa Bake with Tesco Spicy Potato Wedges. Smear some Tesco Free-from Cheese Alternative Creamy Garlic & Herb on the wedges and serve with Tesco Salsa Dip (Cool or Hot) plus a large mixed salad, which can be assembled while the bake and wedges are in the oven.

Waitrose

www.waitrose.com/grocery-delivery T 0800 188 884
Vegan list **www.waitrose.com/specialdiets**
Waitrose sells posh, quality food with a steadily growing free-from range. Gourmet cook ingredients, delicious dried and fresh fruit and lots more – it's a foodie heaven. While some things are pricey, other items are competitive (eg their tinned artichoke hearts are cheaper than the usual and their Essential range is also good value). They also sell Taifun products, including smoked tofu. They don't currently have vegan labelling. Most of their own-brand sugar is vegan.

1. Waitrose Cauliflower & Broccoli Masala
2. Waitrose Spinach & Carrot Pilau
3. Waitrose Bombay Potato
4. Waitrose Tarka Dahl; Waitrose Butterbean Dahl
5. Waitrose Spicy & Warming Vegetable Chilli
6. Waitrose Sweet Potato Curry
7. Waitrose Vegetable Paella
8. Waitrose Love Life Mexican Bean Burger with Salsa
9. Waitrose Chunky Vegetable Quarter Pounders
10. Waitrose Love Life Sweet Potato Chips
11. Waitrose Fresh Soup: Gazpacho; Red Lentil & Chilli; Italian Bean; Tomato, Red Pepper & Chipotle Chilli; Vegetable & Lentil; Spiced Chickpea & Lentil – plus Waitrose Multigrain Croutons!
12. Waitrose Salads: Chickpea & Bean; Fruity Moroccan-style Cous Cous
13. Waitrose Mediterranean Vegetable Pasta Sauce
14. Waitrose Stone Baked Pizza Bases
15. Waitrose Wafer-thin Soft Chinese Pancakes
16. Waitrose Sorbets: Alphonso Mango; Passion Fruit; Sicilian Lemon; Williamette Raspberry; Mango Sorbet Lollies
17. Waitrose Good to Go Elderflower Jelly with Berries

18. Waitrose Summer Puddings
19. Waitrose Baked Goods: Fruit Pies – Apple and Apple & Blackcurrant (individual or large sizes); Iced Finger Bun; Coconut & Cherry Slice
20. Waitrose Belgian Chocolate: Plain; Plain Fruit & Nut

Waitrose Quick Fix Meal 1. Chinese-style Savoury Pancakes. 10-15 minutes

Fry ½-1 pack of Waitrose Crunchy Oriental Stir-fry. Add diced Taifun Smoked Tofu. Meanwhile, warm through Waitrose Soft Chinese Pancakes and Waitrose Plum & Hoisin Stir-fry sauce. Fill the pancakes with the vegetables, tofu and sauce mix. Serve with microwaved Waitrose Essential White Rice (freezer) mixed with Birds Eye Soya Beans (freezer).

Waitrose Quick Fix Meal 2. Indian-style. 10 minutes

Waitrose Sweet Potato Curry; Waitrose Butterbean Dahl; Waitrose Spinach & Carrot Pilau. Serve with Alpro Plain Soya Yoghurt, mango chutney and chapattis.

Waitrose Quick Fix Meal 3. Posh Burger & Chips. 20 minutes

Waitrose Love Life Sweet Potato Chips (freezer) with Waitrose Chunky Vegetable Quarter Pounders. When cooked, lightly smear burgers with Waitrose Coriander & Lemon Tapenade. Serve with a large green salad or steamed green vegetables of your choice.

Superdrug

www.superdrug.com T: 0845 6710709
20 non-food items. They also sell Barry M and GOSH cosmetics – see below.

This high street store is a boon for vegans – its large range of own-brand products is mostly vegan and clearly labelled. Just check these words are on the back of the container: 'suitable for vegetarians and vegans'.

1. Superdrug Mango & Papaya range: Body Butter; Bath Essence; Body Lotion; Body Polish
2. Superdrug Soft range: Gentle Body Lotion; Body & Hand; Hand Therapy; Gradual Tan Body Lotion Medium/Dark etc
3. Superdrug shampoos, Fruity range: Raspberry & Macadamia Nut; Green Apple & Lime; Cherry & Fig (NOT Coconut & Sweet Almond)
4. Superdrug shampoos, Pro Vitamin range: Colour Protect; Full Volume; Hair Defence (NOT Silky Smooth or Daily Nourishment)
5. Superdrug conditioners, Fruity range: Raspberry & Macadamia Nut; Green Apple & Lime; Cherry & Fig (NOT Coconut & Sweet Almond)
6. Superdrug conditioners, Pro Vitamin range: Colour Protect; Full Volume; Hair Defence (NOT Silky Smooth or Daily Nourishment)
7. Superdrug Coconut & Shea range: Butter Shower Cream
8. Superdrug Vitamin E range: Exfoliating Body Scrub; Shimmer Body Lotion
9. Superdrug Essential Wet Wipes: Fragrance-free; Scented
10. Superdrug hair products: Lacquer; Fibre Putty; Matt Clay
11. Superdrug Optimum moisturiser range
12. Superdrug Dry Skin range
13. Superdrug Exfoliating Body Scrub
14. Superdrug Simply Pure range
15. Superdrug Tea Tree range
16. Superdrug BB Cream 5-in-1 Day Cream

17. Superdrug Durban range for men: deodorant; body spray etc
18. Superdrug Solait sun protection range – most is fine, but check on back of container (Sensitive type NOT vegan) AND Superdrug fake tan products – Tinted Bronzing Lotion; Tinted Bronzing Foam; Bronzing Gel; 360˚ Bronzing Spray
19. Superdrug Total Care toothpaste and mouthwash
20. Superdrug razor blades and razors (many razor blades use strips made from animal products)

Barry M at Superdrug
www.barrym.com/fun/animal-friendly
They say: 'all of our products are suitable for vegetarians but some contain animal by-products (like beeswax) making them unsuitable for vegans'. No product labelling yet but information is available on the website – each item has an 'ingredients' link – and the small green V means they are vegan. We have put a small list together for you in the meantime!

LIPS: Glossy Tubes (lip gloss); Lip Lacquer Pencils; Lip Gloss Wands; Lip Liner; Lip Brush (NOT blusher or eye brushes)
FACE: Imperfection Correction Concealer Pen; Shimmer – all range; Natural Dazzle Loose Powder (NOT pressed in a compact)
EYELIDS: Dazzle Dust range: 64, 71, 73, 74, 82, 83, 84, 85, 87, 88, 94, 94, 96, 97, 98, 99, 101; Trio Eye Shadows, all range; Single Pressed Eye Shadows, all range
EYELINERS: Wink Marker Pen; Metallic Eyeliner, all range; Glitter Colour Eyeliner, all range; Liquid Colour Eyeliner
EYELASHES: Black Mascara – Intense Black 3 in 1; Lash Modelling Mascara; Bold Black Waterproof Mascara; Clear Mascara; Colour Mascara; Glitter Lashes
TAN: Perfect Tan Spray Instant; Perfect Tan Mousse Gradual
NAILS: Glitter Nail Paint; All Nail Paints; Croc Nail Effects; Magnetic Nails

GOSH Cosmetics at Superdrug
www.gosh.dk

LIPS: Intense Lip Colour; Velvet Touch Lip Primer; Velvet Touch Lip Liner Waterproof; Long Lasting Lip Marker Pen; Volume Lip Shine

FACE: Natural Touch Foundation; BB Skin Perfection Kit (01 Light & 02 Medium); X-Ceptional Wear Make–Up; Click'N Conceal; Velvet Touch Foundation Primer Classic; Velvet Touch Foundation Primer Anti-Wrinkle Eff

EYELIDS: Mono Eye Shadow (1, 2, 3, 4, 5, 6, 9, 10, 11, 12, 13, 14, 15 & 16); Matt Duo Eye Shadow (Brown Base, Melting Pale & Dark'n Dusky); Smokey Eyes Palette (1 & 2)

EYELINERS: Kohl/Eye Liner (Black, Expresso & White); Eye Liner Pen (Liquid); Long Lasting Eye Liner Pen; Velvet Touch Eye Liner Waterproof (Black Ink, Truly Brown, Hypnotic Grey, Metallic Brass, Pretty Petrol, Woody Green, Lemon Soda, Blue Moon, Alligator, Silver Screen, Sky High, Pure Natural, Classic Grey, Rebellious Brown, I Sea You & Renaissance Gold)

EYELASHES: Amazing Length'n Build Mascara (Not the water-proof ed)

EYEBROWS: Defining Brow Gel; Long Lasting Brow Pen; Eye Brow Pencil

NAILS: Nail Lacquer; Special Ed. Nail Lacquer; Mini Lacqueres

BRONZERS: Bronzing Shimmer Brush; Giant Sun Powder; Bronzing Powder

Viva!

Independent shops

These sites will help you find an independent shop in your area
www.nahs.co.uk (National Association of Health Stores). Or try
**www.freeindex.co.uk/categories/
arts_and_lifestyle/food_and_drink/health_food**

Online stores

These are on the increase so get surfing the web! Many
businesses on our list sell a wide range of products, not just food.
Viva! Shop **www.vivashop.org.uk** – of course! – is a good place
to start for vegan sweeties, wine, chocolate, T-shirts, books, gifts
and lots more.

Alternative Stores **www.alternativestores.com/ethical-shop**
Goodness Direct **www.goodnessdirect.co.uk**
Honest to Goodness **www.honest-to-goodness.org.uk**
Redwood **www.redwoodfoods.co.uk**
Vegan Co **www.vegan.co.uk**
Vegan Store **www.veganstore.co.uk**
Vegan X **www.mailorder.vegancross.co.uk**
Veggiestuff **www.veggiestuff.com**
Vegusto **www.vegusto.co.uk/shop** for their amazing vegan
cheeses, faux meats and more

Other useful resources

Animal Free Shopper – available from Viva! Shop
www.vivashop.org.uk T: 0117 944 1000
www.c-a-l-f.com/easy-vegan an independent website that
provides up to date product information

The internet is a massive resource – full of amazing blogs,
websites, forums, recipes, campaign news and more – and all free.

Products by category

Meat and Fish Alternatives

These are useful products, especially if you are living in a mixed household or just want to throw something vegan on a friend's barbecue!

Quorn in the UK is currently not vegan (it contains egg and sometimes dairy) – but we live in hope, as Quorn USA recently produced a vegan burger.

Gluten-free or wheat-free? Many of the products listed below are suitable for the gluten or wheat intolerant. However, some are not suitable so, as always, check the packet.

Burgers and cutlets

Alicer: Mexican Burgers; Tandoori Burgers; Thai Burgers; Vegetable Burgers

Asda: Nut Cutlets; Spicy Bean and Nacho Burgers; Lemon & Herb Piri Piri Quarter Pounders; Vegetable Goulash Crispbakes; Butternut Squash Quarter Pounders

Biona: Organic Energy Mini Burgers

Clear Spot: Organic Tofu Sesame Burgers; Sesame Burgers

Dragonfly: Beany Organic Cabbage Tatty; Organic Beany Organic Beany Burgers (assorted flavours eg Mushroom, Nut or Vegetable); Mixed Beany Savoury Choice; Savoury Roast Organic Beany

Fry's: Vegetarian Golden Crumbed Schnitzel; Vegetarian Chicken Style Burgers; Vegetarian Traditional Burgers; Vegetarian Spiced Burgers

Goodlife Fairtrade – all their range is now vegan: Nut Cutlets; Fruity Falafel Quarter Pounders; Garden Vegetable Quarter Pounders; Spicy Bean Quarter Pounders

Grassingtons: Spicy Bean Burgers; Vegetable Burgers

Linda McCartney: Vegetable Roasties

Provamel: Meat-free; Organic Tofu Burgers with Vegetables;

Organic Tofu Burgers; Organic Tofu Schnitzels
Redwood: Gourmet Meat-Free Quarter Pounder; Vegideli Organic Schnitzels
Sainsbury's: Spicy Bean Quarter Pounders; Vegetable Burgers; Vegetarian Nut Cutlets
Taifun: Cutlets, with either Corn & Pepper, Spelt & Sunflower or Tofu, Hazelnut and Green Spelt
Vegetarian Choice: Vegetable Protein Burgers; Lincolnshire Sausages
Viana: Veggie Wiener Schnitzel; Cowgirl Veggie Steaks; Bonanza Veggie Steaks

Dried Products: mixes and TVP (textured vegetable protein)

Dried mixes used to be all that was available and many people have ditched these products for ready-made sausages, burgers etc. However, they are cheaper than frozen or chilled products, are a good pantry staple – and great for camping trips! Use them to make rissoles, burgers, sausages, stuffed veggies. Try adding a splash of wine for a treat!

Mixes
Asda: Meat-free dried mixes: Mexican Chilli; Sausage; Falafel; Lincolnshire Sausage; Burger Mix
Essential: Sosmix dried – assorted flavours
Granose: Burger Mixes (various); Sausage Mixes (various); Nut Roasts (various)

TVP
Soya-based, this product comes in two colours – pale beige (plain) and brown (flavoured) – and is sold as mince or chunks. Whichever you use, enhance the flavour by soaking in concentrated hot stock first. Can be used in savoury dishes to replace meat, eg Shepherd's Pie, 'Chicken' curry, pies etc

Suma: TVP Chunks; TVP Flavoured Chunks; TVP Flavoured Mince;
TVP Mince
Own-brands: chunks and mince sold in health food shops

Fish-style
Clearspot: Organic Sea Cakes
Redwood: Vegetarian Breaded Fish-style Fingers; Fishless Steaks;
Scampi-style Pieces; Thai Fish-style Cakes

Meat-style pieces
Asda: Chicken-style Pieces
Fry's: Vegetarian Chicken-style Strips; Vegetarian Chicken-style
Nuggets; Vegetarian Beef-style Strips
Realeat: Meat-Free Chicken-style Pieces
Redwood: Chorizo-style Chunks; Vegi-Deli Chicken-style Pieces;
Vegi-Deli Organic Nuggets
Viana: Chickin Frikassee, Nuggets and Fillets

Mince
Most veggie mince is vegan – but not Quorn

Asda: Vegetarian Mince
Fry's: Vegetarian Mince
Linda McCartney: Vegetarian Mince
Redwood: Vegideli Vegetarian Mince
Sainsbury's: Meat-free Mince
Tesco: Meat-free Mince

Pâté
Granovita: a range, including Spicy Mexican Organic; Organic
Tangy Tomato Pâté
Le Sojami: Fresh Soy Pâté: Olive; Seaweed
Redwood Vegideli: Beanfeast; Organic Brussels-style; Gourmet
Mushroom; Making Waves Tuna-Style; Duck-style & Orange

San Amvrosia: Spicy Pinto Bean Dip
Taifun: Pâté Verdi
Tartex Organic: a range, including Chilli Yeast Pâté; Sundried Tomato
Tartex non-organic: a range, including Roasted Onion & Pink Peppercorn; Olive and Garlic
Viana Tofu Crème: a range, including Papricanon; Pepper; Home Style; Veggie Garden

Roasts & bakes
Dragonfly: Tatty – Potato and Rice Cake
Goodlife: Bistro Root Vegetable Roast; Hearty Vegetable Bakes; Spicy Lentil & Vegetable Wedge; Spinach & Lentil Grill
Grassingtons: Multigrain Vegetable Bakes
Redwood: Cheatin' Roast, Turkey or Beef; Cheatin' Celebration Roast

Sausages
Dragonfly: Organic Soysage
Fry's: Braai Flavour; Traditional; Hot Dogs; Veg Express Sausage Rolls; Vegetarian Poloni
Goodlife: Glamorgan Sausages
Linda McCartney: Sausages; Sausage Rolls
Redwood: Gourmet Sage & Marjoram; Hot Dog Style; Organic Oregano & Basil; Organic Curry Sausages; Organic Frankfurter Style; Pork Style; Vegideli Lincolnshire Style
Taifun: Organic Grill Sausages, also with herbs; Organic Mini Weiner/Frankfurters; Organic Tofu Weiner/Frankfurters; Puszta Wiener Hungarian Style
Vegetarian Choice: Lincolnshire Sausages; Vegetable Protein Sausages
Wicken Fen: New Recipe Cumberland Sausages; Gourmet Sausages: Mushroom & Tarragon; Tomato & Garlic; Country Herb; Tasty Mexicana; Mediterranean Roasted Vegetable; Cumberland Style; Apple & Sage and Gluten-free Carrot & Coriander

L-Plate
Vegan

RAISE A GLASS *Viva!*

Did you know many wine producers use animal-derived agents during the clarifying and fining process? Not in our wines – we are passionate about organic, animal-free tipples!

Viva!'s Wine Club stocks over 350 award-winning vegan wines, beers and spirits. Ranging from oaky Chardonnays to citrusy Rieslings and spicy Merlots to plummy Pinot Noirs.

To order a cruelty-free case of wine, simply visit **www.viva.org.uk/wineshop** or call **0117 944 1000** (Mon-Fri, 9am-6pm)

Bodacious Balms *Viva!* for Luscious Lips

Keep your smackers moisturised and smelling sweet with the Viva! Shop's hand-picked range of vegan lip balms. No beeswax, preservatives or nasty chemicals, our balms are made with silky shea butter, vitamin E and essential oils for maximum creaminess and kiss-ability.

Order online **www.vivashop.org.uk** or call **0117 944 1000** (Mon-Fri, 9am-6pm)

43

Seitan and gluten

Seitan (pronounced 'Satan'!) and gluten are the same thing. It is made from wheat protein and is a high-protein meat replacement that has been used in Asia for thousands of years. Chinese restaurants that offer a 'Buddhist vegetarian' menu often use it. Western veggie chefs use it in pies, roasts or slices. It is tasty and nutritious but obviously not suitable for the wheat and gluten intolerant.

Companion: Mock Duck, Mock Chicken etc – available in tins from Oriental supermarkets
Granose: Mock Duck
Lima: Seitan
Mong Lee Shang: Braised Gluten – see Companion brand
Primal Strips: Jerky
Viana: Seitan
Yakso: Seitan

Slices and Rashers

Redwood: Cheatin' Slices: Ham; Chicken; Beef; Garlic Sausage; Pepperoni; Turkey, Sage and Onion
Redwood: Streaky-style Vegetarian Rashers; Vegideli Organic Vegetarian Rashers
Vegusto Sandwich Slices: Lion-style; Dill; Smoked; Deli-style; Mediterranean-style

Tempeh

Tempeh originates from Indonesia. It is a natural product made by fermenting soya bean cakes – high in protein, with an interesting taste and texture. We like it fried in rashers with soya sauce – but try using chunks in a curry sauce, too.

Doctor Tempeh: sells organic tinned tempeh in a traditional curry sauce, made in Indonesia from local spices and organic soya beans

Fresh Tempeh: online from **www.freshtempeh.co.uk**
Impulse Foods: frozen – Plain or Herb & Garlic; Organic Smoky
Slices; fresh – Plain; Hemp Seeds; Sea Vegetables
Redwood: Tempeh Rashers
Viana: Tempeh

Tofu

Tofu is also called beancurd and has also been eaten in Asia for
thousands of years. It is a nutritious and highly versatile food that
comes in different types, textures and flavours. Tofu is made from
soya beans, water and a natural coagulating agent which
transforms the fresh soya milk into curds. Then these curds are
weighted down and drained to make the tofu – a very similar
process to how dairy cheese is made!

- Medium and firm regular tofu – use in stir-fries, Thai curries
  etc
- Silken (soft-firm) – use
  in cheesecakes,
  mousses, sauces,
  quiches etc
- Flavoured – marinated
  pieces; smoked; basil;
  sun-dried tomato etc –
  cut into chunks or thin
  slices. Use cold or heat
  up and add to other
  dishes just before
  serving. Smoked tofu
  can be fried up in slices
  until quite crispy – add
  a splash of soya sauce
  just before serving

Viva!

Blue Dragon: Firm and Extra-Firm Silken Tofu
Cauldron: Organic Marinated Tofu Pieces; Original Tofu
Clearspot: Organic Tofu; Naturally Smoked Tofu; Marinated Tofu
Danival: Organic Lentils and Tofu with Vegetables
Dragonfly Tofu: Natural; Smoked; Deep Fried
Marigold: Braised Tofu (tinned)
Morinaga: Silken Tofu, assorted types
Mori-Nu Silken Style Tofu: Soft; Firm; Extra-Firm
Taifun Organic: Tofu Rosso (sundried tomatoes); Basil Tofu; Smoked Tofu; Smoked Tofu with Almonds & Sesame Seeds; Olive; Silken
Viana: Real Nigari Tofu; Real Smoked Tofu; Hazelnut Tofu; Sprout Tofu

Oriental supermarkets: (Chinese, Vietnemese, Korean etc). For good quality and good value tofu (plain, firm or silken). Look out for organic or at least non-GM on the label. Unicurd brand is non-GM and also sells an organic range.

La Maison du Vert
vegetarian hotel & restaurant

Our non-smoking hotel & restaurant is set in a stunning Normandy valley within 3 acres of beautiful gardens.

eat

- **Delicious vegetarian and vegan gourmet menus**
- **Naturally grown produce, organic wines, ciders and beers.**

∞ Visit Monet's garden, Bayeux, Honfleur, Camembert & more
∞ Chateaux, markets, gardens, beaches, picturesque towns
∞ Walk, cycle, relax!

rest

Contact: Debbie & Daniel Armitage
61120 Ticheville, Normandy, France
00 33 2 33 36 95 84
Email: mail@maisonduvert.com

www.maisonduvert.com

see

Ready-made foods

Bread

Most standard bread is suitable for vegans but there are some exceptions.

- Many breads from the Co-op, Hovis and Warburton are vegan and are labelled if so
- Pitta bread is always vegan
- Wraps – some are fine (including Lidl) but again, check!
- Naan bread – see below
- When buying fresh from a bakery – independent, high street or in-store – always ask. They will carry an allergens list

Things to avoid

- Added products like milk, yoghurt (usually in naan bread), buttermilk, milk powder, whey, butter, Amino L-cysteine (an animal derivative) and honey
- Butter-based bread like brioche and croissants (although JusRol Croissant Mix and Pain au Chocolate are both vegan)
- Cheese-bread
- 'Luxury' breads which might contain non-vegan extras
- Naan bread – usually contains yoghurt or milk powder. But these are vegan:
  - Newbury Philips Bakery (distributed by Essential)
  - Tesco Light Choices 6 Mini Naan Bread

Also, some ethnic grocers sell vegan naan, so it's worth checking!

Breakfast cereal

This isn't a definitive list – the range of cereals continues to expand – but it will get you started! When in doubt, check a company's website or give them a call.

Asda: Asda Cranberry Wheats; Asda Organic Bran Flakes; Asda Organic Muesli; Asda Whole Wheat Bisks; Asda Malted Wheaties; Asda Smartprice Cornflakes; Asda 55% Fruit Muesli

Co-op: Co-operative Farms Porridge Oats; Cornflakes; Easy Oats; Fruit & Nut Muesli; Mixed Fruit Muesli; Porridge Oats; Wholewheat Biscuits

Doves Farm: Chewy Rice Pop & Chocolate Cakes; Cornflakes; Wholewheat Cereal Biscuits

Essential Wholefoods: lots of their mueslis and also two lovely sugar and honey-free granolas – Hazelnut Crunch and Sultana Crunch

Jordans: Organic Flakes & Berries; Organic Fruit & Fibre; Superfoods Breakfast Flakes; Country Crisp – Four Nut Combo; Luxury Raisin and more, including many of their mueslis

Kellogg's: Fruit & Fibre; Raisin Wheat; Just Right; Rice Krispies Multigrain; Frosties

M&S: Count on Us Fruit & Nut Muesli; Organic Crunchy Sultana Granola; Exotic Fruit & Nut Muesli; Organic Luxury Fruit & Nut Muesli

- Avoid Swiss-style mueslis like Alpen or supermarket 'Swiss' own-brands as they usually contain milk derivatives
- Plain oats – porridge or jumbo – are vegan by nature; it's only when other ingredients are added that you need to get label-spotting
- Fortified cereals are an easy way to increase one's intake of plant-based iron and other vitamins. However, beware of Vitamin D3, which is not vegan. (Sometimes it is listed as just Vitamin D.) It is frustrating, because Vitamin D2 is plant-based but manufacturers are sticking to D3. However, D2 and a vegan D3 are now available – see page 90

Nature's Path: Crispy Rice; Mesa Sunrise; Millet Rice etc. They say 'Most of our products are suitable for vegans, but if they contain milk-containing ingredients such as milk chocolate or honey then they are not.'

Orgran: Gluten-free Muesli; Rice Porridge

Quaker: Oat Crisp; Oat Crunch; Oat Hoops; Puffed Wheat; all their basic porridges and also the Simple (quick cook) range – Golden Syrup; Original; Fruit Muesli Flavour

Readybrek: Original

Sainsbury's: Wholewheat Biscuits; Wholegrain Apricot Wheats; Wholegrain Raisin Wheats; Malties; Be Good To Yourself less than 3% Fat High Fruit Muesli; Pecan & Maple Crisp Cereal; Fruit & Nut Muesli; Wholegrain Blueberry Wheats; Breakfast Wholewheat Biscuits; Express Porridge Original, Golden Syrup, Apple & Cinnamon, Butterscotch; SO Organic Express Porridge Original

Waitrose: Wholewheat Biscuits; Fruit & Nut Muesli

Weetabix: Crunchy Bran; Mini Crunch Fruit & Nut Weetabix; Organic Weetabix; Original

Canned savoury food (not soup)

Baked beans and spaghetti hoops – most brands are fine but always check ingredients.

Amy's Kitchen: Chilli – medium or spicy

Supermarkets: Many pulse and vegetable-based tinned meals are suitable, eg

- **Asda**: Vegetable Ravioli; Chickpea Dahl; Vegetable Balti; Vegetable Chilli
- **Sainsbury's**: Vegetarian Spaghetti Bolognese; Vegetable Chilli
- **M&S**: Mixed Vegetable Curry; Three Bean Chilli
- **Tesco**: Vegetable Chilli; Tesco Ratatouille

Pastry

Pastry is sold in frozen blocks (defrost first then roll out) or in chilled, ready-rolled sheets.

- JusRol – all their range is vegan (except for All Butter and Sweet Shortcrust). That means the rest of their range – puff, shortcrust and filo – is OK! Their vol-au-vent cases make good buffet food with a vegan creamy mushroom filling – and their pain au chocolate is vegan too
- Sainsbury's and Tesco each sell their own vegan range – ready-rolled shortcrust pastry (regular and light) and the same for puff. Check with other supermarkets' vegan lists
- Filo pastry of all brands is nearly always vegan. Instead of using butter in a recipe, use vegan margarine, olive oil or oil spray

Pasta and noodles

- Dried pasta is usually vegan. The exceptions are some noodles such as Chinese egg noodles or Italian tagliatelle (although not all tagliatelle contains egg so check the label).
- Rice noodles – fresh or dried – are nearly always vegan.
- Fresh pasta usually contains egg

Pies and Pasties

Clive's Pies: most of their range is vegan and includes Chestnut Cassoulet and Arabian Chickpea. Sold in health food shops and online

Forest Foods: Vegetarian Thai Wrap; Vegetarian Smokey Vegetable Burrito – Goodness Direct mail order and some Manchester outlets

Holland & Barrett: Vegetarian Jumbo Sos Roll; H&B Porkless Pie

Linda McCartney: Country Pies; Mushroom & Ale Pies

Redwood: Beef-style Pasties

VegOut: slices (Holland & Barrett)

Ready meals

Fry's: Veg Express Cottage Pie

Innocent Veg Pots. Most of these are vegan and widely available in major supermarkets

Linda McCartney: Vegetarian Sausage & Bean Stew; Chilli Non Carne with Rice

Simply Organic: Pure & Pronto: Vegetable Casserole

Supermarkets: most sell a small range of vegan own-brand ready meals or side dishes – these are often Indian. Just watch out for added butter, yoghurt and cream etc

Salad

There are too many types to list individually. However:

- mixed leaf bags are usually vegan, although sachets of dressing might not be
- mixed salads – eg grain or pulse-based are delicious and there are quite a few to choose from. Just check there is no added feta, parmesan, honey and such
- avoid coleslaw/mayo-based salads and anything else with cheese, yoghurt, honey etc. See our supermarket lists for a good selection. And see page 62 for Salad Dressings. However, it takes only a few minutes to make your own coleslaw – grate a bit of white cabbage and carrot, add some chopped spring onion and mix thoroughly with vegan mayo (thinned down with a little soya or rice milk) plus salt and pepper.

Savoury snacks

- Falafels
- Indian vegetarian snacks – pakoras, samosas, onion bhajis
- Chinese vegetarian spring rolls

All these are usually fine and make a great standby for parties and celebrations. Just check that nothing odd like milk has been added! A vegan-suitable range is available in just about every supermarket, as well as some health food shops.

Soup

Soup is usually sold as fresh or tinned. Either way you will find plenty of vegan flavours to choose from. Beware anything that says 'cream of' as it often contains – surprise! – cream or milk.

Fresh soup – supermarket own brands tend to be the best overall.

Asda: see page 15
Co-op: see page 17
Covent Garden: Tomato, Vegetable & Lentil; Minestrone; Plum Tomato & Basil; Caribbean Sweet Potato; Moroccan Tagine
M&S: see page 22-23
Sainsbury's: Minestrone; Tomato & Basil; Tomato, Lentil & Red Pepper; Tomato, Roasted Vegetable & Olive; Spicy Mexican Bean & Chipotle Chilli; Organic Vegetable & Barley; Organic Red Lentil; Mexican Tomato Salsa
Tesco: Tomato & Basil; Minestrone; Tesco Finest Puy Lentil & Vine Ripened Tomato; Chilli Bean; Lentil, Bean & Barley; Tesco Finest Bean, Corn & Chipotle Soup
Waitrose: Tomato & Fresh Basil; Gazpacho; Red Lentil & Chilli; Italian Bean; Tomato, Red Pepper & Chipotle Chilli; Vegetable & Lentil; Spiced Chickpea & Lentil. See page 33

Tinned soup – the same rules apply so check the label. Amy's Kitchen range is particularly good and tastes much fresher than most tins and each supermarket will sell one or two vegan soups in its tinned range.

Dairy and egg alternatives

Cheese

Vegan cheese has improved vastly over the years, as has the range of products and flavours available. There is no vegan Brie yet but who knows…?

Mozzarisella: vegan mozzarella that melts. www.mozzarisella.co.uk
Redwood hard cheese: Cheezly comes in at least nine assorted flavours including Mozzarella, Blue, Cheddar and a rather good Parmy-style. Melting Cheezly is also available in Mozzarella (good for pizza) and more. There is also a soya-free variety – and a Christmas selection pack – as well as slices in selected flavours
Sheese hard cheese: eleven flavours such as Smoked Cheddar and Cheshire. Plus two Melty flavours: Mild Cheddar and Red Cheddar
Sheese creamy: five flavours including Original (good for cheesecake) to Garlic & Herb
Tesco: see page 31
Tofutti creamy cheese: six flavours including Original (excellent for cheesecake); Garlic & Herb; Olive
Tofutti: Creamy Smooth Slices (Mozzarella and Cheddar); and grated Mozzarella – good for pizzas etc
Veganic: assorted types, available online and selected stores www.veganicfoods.co.uk
Vegusto No-Moo: this Swiss company sells seven delicious flavours including Piquant (a bit like Parmesan); Walnut; Melty and No-Moo Sauce – a ready-made cheese sauce

Cream

Alpro: single pouring cream, soya-based
Granovita: Cremovita – soya-based thick whipping cream
Ecomil: Cuisine – almond-based single cream
Oatly: oat-based single cream

Viva!

Provamel: see Alpro
Sojatoo: Whipping Cream (rice or soya) – in cartons or spray cans
Tofutti Sour Supreme: soya-based sour cream

Custard
Cartons
- Alpro
- Provamel

Powder
Birds and most supermarket own-brands are suitable.

To make vegan custard:
1. Follow the instructions on the tub, but replace the cows' milk with a plant milk of your choice.
2. Reduce the plant milk to 450ml if you want thick custard (instead of the 570ml/pint on the packet instructions).
3. Taste and add more sugar if necessary – stir well until it has dissolved in the heat.
4. If the custard is too thick just add a bit more liquid and mix in well!

Egg
Ener-G egg replacer: a replacement raising agent used in baking
Orgran egg replacer: as Ener-G
Vegg: this can be used in baking too. However, it has more of an eggy flavour, so can be used in other ways. See
www.veganrecipeclub.org.uk and Vegg's own website for recipes

Linseed, also called flax seed: 1 tbsp finely ground linseed mixed with 2 tbsp water is the equivalent to one egg. Use it as a binder in cakes (not a raising agent). Don't use more than this amount in any one cake as it will taste too strong. It can also be bought ready-ground – look for flax meal or linseed meal

Scrambled tofu is delicious and easy to make. Again, check out www.veganrecipeclub.org.uk for a good recipe

Margarine
Biona: Spread
Co-op: Soft Spread
M&S: Sunflower Spread; Sunflower Spread Light Dairy Free
Pure: Soya or Sunflower – available in many supermarkets
Sainsbury's: Free-from Spread
Suma: Soya or Sunflower
Tesco: Free-from Soya Spread
Vitalite: Dairy-free Spread

Milk
Soya milk: plain; flavoured (chocolate, banana or strawberry); sweetened; unsweetened; long-life; fresh; organic; fortified – an easy way to get calcium, B12 etc. Each type tastes different so you may need to try a few first – some people prefer long-life, others favour fresh

Grain milks
Rice milk: plain; fortified; plain and chocolate. Rice Dream is the main brand but there are others
Other grain milks: oat; quinoa – mainly Oatly or Ecomil brands

Nut or seed milks: almond; coconut; hazel; hemp – mainly Ecomil and Kara brands but there are others too

Alternatives to dairy milk are made from soya, nuts or grains.

The most common brands are:

Alpro: mostly sold in supermarkets. They sell a big range, which also includes yoghurts, pouring crème, soya desserts and more
Ecomil: almond, hazelnut etc
Granovita: soya milk
Kara: coconut milk which is sold either chilled or fresh. Both types are fortified
Plamil: the first soya milk producer in the UK! Their soya milk is organic and was voted best-buy by *Ethical Consumer* magazine
Provamel: Alpro's sister group, mostly sold in health food shops. It has a similar range to Alpro
So-good: fresh soya milk, assorted flavours including chocolate
Soya Soleil: soya milk
Supermarkets: each sells at least one type of own-brand range of soya milk, usually long-life; they may also sell fresh and a 'value' long-life. Supermarkets such as Tesco are also starting to sell own-brand plant milks such as coconut or hazelnut in their free-from range

Yoghurt
Plain, fruity and pouring yoghurt is available in larger supermarkets as well as health food shops and delis. These are mostly soya but Co-Yo is coconut-based.

Alpro: 500ml tubs of plain, vanilla, pouring, fruit; individual four-packs of fruity yoghurt
Co-Yo: coconut based yoghurt, assorted flavours
Granovita: Soyage, assorted flavours
Provamel: see Alpro
Redwood: assorted flavours
Tesco: see page 31

Sauces, dressings, dips and condiments

Condiments

Cranberry sauce and jelly: nearly always vegan. Many brands!
Engevita: nutritional yeast flakes. A vegan must-have, it is a nutty, slightly cheesy-flavoured delight which is also rich in B vitamins. Not to be confused with brewer's yeast or yeast extract. It is currently available only from health food shops. However, it can be bought online at most of the stores we list on page 37 but also on Amazon and E-bay! Use to make cheesy sauces; sprinkle on pasta dishes, soup or just about anything. Also available with added vitamin B12
Mustard: Dijon, English, French and Wholegrain have different flavours and are all useful for making sauces and vinaigrettes – the mellower Dijon in particular. Mustard is nearly always vegan but check for honey, whey etc

Cooking sauces

This is not a full list, just a handful of what is available. Basically, every brand – including supermarkets – sells some sauces that are vegan-friendly. For reasons of space we haven't listed every company – but their websites will help – and if not, try customer services.

Meridian: nearly all their range is vegan. Sauces include: Free-from Creamy Mushroom & White Wine; Free-from Creamy Sundried Tomato; Organic Tomato & Mushroom Pasta Sauce; Organic Tomato & Olive Pasta Sauce; Free-from Green Pesto; Free-from Green Thai Sauce.

British

Asda: Sausage Casserole Cooking Sauce

Chinese

Asda: Black Bean and Chilli Stir-fry; Chow Mein Stir-fry; Plum and Ginger Stir-fry; Szechuan Stir-fry; Extra Special Hoisin

Blue Dragon (jars): Hoi Sin; Black Bean; Sweet & Sour; Sweet Chilli; Szechuan Tomato; Chinese Mushroom & Garlic; Sweet Soy & Roasted Red Chilli

Blue Dragon (sachets): Sweet & Sour; Peking Lemon; Szechuan Tomato; Hoi Sin & Garlic

Co-op: Black Bean Cook-in

Tesco: Black Bean & Roasted Garlic Stir-fry; Finest Tamarind, Fresh Lime & Chilli Stir-fry; Limited Edition Szechuan Stir-fry; Chinese Style Barbecue Stir-fry; Singapore Style Stir-fry

> Avoid oyster sauce in ready-made sauces but see page 62 for a vegan version. Sometimes dairy products or honey are added to sauces, depending on the brand.

Indian

Asda: Jalfrezi; Madras; Rogan Josh; Vindaloo; Extra Special Balti

Loyd Grossman: Balti; Jalfrezi; Bhuna; Dopiaza

Patak's: their lactic acid is vegan, so several in their range are suitable

Patak's (cooking sauces): Balti; Jalfrezi; Madras; Rogan Josh; Vindaloo; Creamy Coconut & Peanut; Creamy Coconut & Pineapple Cooking Sauce; Oven Bake Biryani Sauce; Tomato & Cumin

Patak's (pastes): Bhuna; Bombay Potato Curry Paste; Biryani; Madras; Mild Curry; Rogan Josh; Tikka; Tikka Masala; Vindaloo

Sainsbury's Cooking Sauces: Balti; Jalfrezi; Madras; Bhuna; Rogan Josh; Vindaloo

> Avoid dairy products (cream, butter, yoghurt, milk etc) in some sauces and pastes like Tikka Masala and Korma.

L-Plate
Vegan

Italian

Asda: Bolognese Pasta; Spicy Tomato Pasta; Tomato & Chunky Vegetable Pasta; Tomato & Garlic Pasta; Tomato & Olive Stir-through Pasta; Extra Special Sundried Tomato & Garlic Pasta Sauce

Co-op: Healthier Choice Tomato & Herb Pasta Sauce; Hot & Spicy Pasta Sauce

Loyd Grossman: Tomato & Basil; Tomato & Roast Garlic; Tomato & Chilli; Tomato & Sweet Red Pepper; Primavera

Seggiano: Cream of Zucchini; Tomato Sugo Pasta Sauce

Tesco Fresh: Arrabbiata; Tomato & Basil; Cherry Tomato; Chargrilled Vegetable

Waitrose: Chargrilled Vegetable with Olives

> Basic and vegetable-based tomato sauces are usually fine. Avoid those with added cream or cheese (Marscapone, Parmesan etc). Some contain added wine that may or may not be vegan.

Japanese

Asda: Teriyaki Stir-fry

Tesco: Teriyaki Stir-fry; Japanese Seven Spice Stir-fry Shot

Mexican

Most are fine but check there is no added cheese or cream.

Co-op: Hot Chilli Cook-in

Discovery: Fajita; Enchilada

Loyd Grossman: Chilli; Fiery Chilli

Thai

Asda: Green Thai Curry; Red Thai Curry; Organic Green Thai Curry Cooking Sauce

Viva!

Biona: Thai Style Organic Curry Paste
M&S: Red Thai Curry Sauce; Green Thai Curry Sauce
Sainsbury's: Free-from Thai Green Curry Cooking Sauce
Thai Taste: Green and Red Curry Pastes (and kits) are vegan

> Avoid fish sauce or even cream – although coconut milk is fine.

Dipping sauces
Blue Dragon: Thai Chilli; Hot Chilli; Sweet Chilli – available everywhere
Sharwoods: Plum Sauce – available everywhere
Sweet Mandarin: Sweet & Sour; Barbecue; Sweet Chilli – available on Sainsbury's free-from shelves and Selfridges

Dips
Hummus: available everywhere – supermarkets, health food shops and delis. It is nearly always vegan but honey is added to some brands of Moroccan hummus
Salsa: fresh tomato salsa and salsa in jars is usually vegan
Guacamole: most supermarket versions contain cream so make your own in a minute. Mash up 1-2 'ready to eat' avocados with a fork, add a little crushed garlic plus lime juice and salt to taste. Result!

Gravy
Asda: Onion Gravy Granules; Vegetable Gravy Granules; Extra Special Onion Gravy
Bisto: Gravy Granules Favourite; Gravy Granules Favourite Reduced Salt; Onion Granules
Kallo: Just Bouillon Vegetable Gravy Granules
Redwood: Cheatin Instant Gravy Powder
Tesco: Everyday Value Gravy Granules; Vegetable Gravy Granules
Sainsbury's: Gravy Granules for Vegetarian Dishes

Mayonnaise
See salad dressings on page 62.

Pesto
Vegan pesto uses nuts (and sometimes nutritional yeast) instead of cheese.

Biona: Organic Green Pesto
Meridian: Free From Green Pesto
Sacla: Char-Grilled Aubergine Pesto
Seggiano: Raw Basil Pesto Genovese; Red Pesto Sauce; Cime de Rapa (turnip top greens!) – not cheap but some the best pesto we've ever tasted
Suma: Organic Vegan Green and Red
Zest: Organic Vegan Basil Pesto; Coriander, Basil & Hazelnut Pesto-Style Sauce

Pickle and chutney
Many pickles are vegan by nature – just check the labels. There are lots of them about in every supermarket and shop, from 'modern' pickles to ethnic (mango etc) to the more traditional like Branston's and piccalilli. We don't have room for them all so here are a few favourites. The main thing to watch out for is lactic acid, some of which is vegan, some not.

Branston: Yes! Own-brand Branston equivalents would be Ploughman or Sweet Pickle – check product labels
Patak's: lovely things to eat with your curry. Brinjal (aubergine) is a favourite but there are plenty more, as well as the ubiquitous mango
Sainsbury's: Red Onion Chutney; Piccalilli and many more
Tesco: Spicy Lime Pickle; Spicy Mango Chutney; Mango Chutney; Finest Mango Chutney; Discounter Mango Chutney

Salad dressing

Mayonnaise

Many of the brands listed below sell standard mayonnaise plus flavoured varieties

Mayola (Granovita brand): sold in health food shops and Tesco
Plamil: health food shops and other – from a dedicated vegan company – Plain; Garlic; Tarragon and Chilli
Solesse: Asda
Tiger Tiger: Sainsbury's

Salad Cream

Asda: Light Salad Cream
Granovita: Salad Cream

Vinaigrette

This isn't a comprehensive list. However, many types of vinaigrette are intrinsically vegan – just keep an eye out for added honey and such.

Asda: Good For You Italian-style; Good For You Lemon & Black Pepper
Newman's Own: Lighten Up Balsamic; Lighten Up French
Kraft: Light Balsamic; Light Italian
Sainsbury's: Be Good to Yourself French Style
Tesco: Light Choices Balsamic
Waitrose: French; Italian; Alphonso Mango, Chilli & Pineapple; Essentials Vinaigrette

Table sauce

Brown sauce: and fruity brown sauce is almost always vegan.
Oyster sauce: Lee Kum Kee Vegetarian Stir-fry Sauce, from Oriental stores (other types include oysters or other fish). Or see **www.veganrecipeclub.org.uk** for a simple, five minute recipe

Tomato sauce/ketchup: usually vegan – Heinz, Sainsbury's, Tesco etc are fine. Just check there is no added milk, dried milk or whey
Worcester sauce: Life or Biona (mainstream brands contain fish – anchovy)
BBQ sauce: usually fine but always check

Viva!

Sweet stuff

Biscuits

Asda: Asda Morning Coffee; Asda Rich Tea; Asda Rich Tea Fingers; Asda Free-from Chocolate Chip; Asda Smartprice Bourbon; Asda Smartprice Fruit Shortie; Asda Smartprice Ginger Nuts

Dove's Farm: Organic Lemon Cookies; Apple & Sultana Flapjack; Fruity Organic Oat

Hobnobs: plain and choc chip are vegan (but dark chocolate are not); many supermarket own brand plain oat biscuits are also vegan)

McVities Light Digestives: (not regular)

Nairn's: Fruit & Spice; Mixed Berries Oat; Stem Ginger

Sainsbury's: Ginger Snaps; Rich Tea Finger; Morning Coffee; Basics Ginger; Oaty; Sainsbury's Digestives

Tesco: no biscuits were included in their vegan list, but this is probably because of the allergens/mixed production line issue (see page 14). However, we looked carefully at the ingredients in their own-brand range. Many seem vegan-friendly. Everyday Value Bourbon Creams; Everyday Value Digestives (not Tesco Digestives); Everyday Value Ginger Nuts; Everyday Value Rich Tea; Everyday Value Nice; Tesco Bourbons; Tesco Ginger nuts; Tesco Fruit Shortcake; Tesco Oaties

Waitrose: Rich Tea; Fruity Shortcake; Digestive; Shortcake; Ginger nuts; Reduced Fat Rich Tea; Squashed Fruit

Cakes, pastries and baking

Shop-bought

Sadly, most shop cakes are not vegan although there is a handful available.

Happy Kitchen: assorted flavours from www.goodnessdirect.co.uk

JusRol: Pain au Chocolate – sold in a tub, bake for a few minutes. Very good!

Mrs Crimble: Dutch Fruit Cake (H&B and supermarket free-from shelves)

Vegan outlets

Vegan cakes are popping up in our larger towns and cities or online. If your local café doesn't sell vegan cake, offer them a recipe – preferably with a slice for them to sample! – and encourage them to do so. If the cake is good everyone will eat it, not just the vegans.

Ms Cupcake in Brixton: awesome!
Café Kino in Bristol: legendary cakes and food, all vegan. The café estimates that 80 per cent of its customers are not vegan yet love all the vegan food, including cakes.

And lots more…

Online bakeries:
www.hannahbananabakery.co.uk – mail order or direct in Southampton
www.theheavenlycakecompany.co.uk/vegan-cake
www.psitsvegan.co.uk
www.rebeccas-cakes.co.uk
www.vegancakedirect.co.uk
And there are plenty more, so search the web!

Home-made
Cheaper and fun to do! It also makes you very popular…

From scratch
See the dedicated baking section on **www.veganrecipeclub.org.uk** as well as lots of recipes. The Luscious Vegan Sponge Cake has many fans, as does the Coffee & Walnut – but there are plenty more. Alternatively, try one of the current range of vegan baking books, many sold by the Viva! Shop **www.vivashop.org.uk/catalog/book-**

club/vegan-baking. We love *Vegan Cupcakes Take Over the World*
by Isa Chandra Moskowitz and Terry Hope Romero!

From a packet
Asda: Kids' Baking Ginger Cookie Dough with Currants; Rainbow
Hundreds & Thousands; Natural Food Colours – blue, green, red

Betty Crocker: Chocolate Fudge Brownie Mix
Replace the egg in their packet recipe with 1 tsp egg replacer
plus ONE of these

- ¼ cup apple sauce OR
- 1 small banana, mashed well OR
- 1 small sweet potato, peeled, cooked and mashed well

The Co-op Chocolate Cake Mix
Add
- 1 medium-large banana, well-mashed
- ½ tsp baking powder
- 90-100ml soya or other dairy-free milk

Find out how to make it **www.veganrecipeclub.org.uk/vegan-
cooking-blog/choc-cake-co-op**

Sainsbury's: Madeira Cake Mix; Spiced Apple Cake Mix
Lightly oil the cake tin and line the base with greaseproof paper, then:

Sainsbury's Madeira Cake: replace eggs, milk and butter with:
- 75g vegan margarine – soften in the microwave for just a
  few seconds. Pure, Biona, Vitalite, Suma and Sainsbury's
  Free-From spread are all vegan
- 1 tsp baking powder
- 160ml soya milk
- 1 tbsp flax meal mixed with 2 tbsp water

Sainsbury's Spiced Apple Cake: replace the egg with:

- 1 tbsp flax meal mixed with 1 tbsp cold water
- 1½ tsp egg replacer
- 60g vegan margarine, softened
- 45-50ml water or soya milk

See also www.veganrecipeclub.org.uk

Chocolate

You can still eat milk chocolate – the vegan version! It's usually made from rice milk and is quite widely available, as is vegan white chocolate. Useful places to look are supermarket free-from shelves, good health food shops and online stores like Viva! (see page 38 for a list).

Booja Booja: a dedicated vegan company which sells a range of sumptuous, organic and fairtrade truffles

Dairy-free: milk chocolate style buttons sold in most supermarkets

Kinnerton: Dairy-free, Egg-free, Gluten and Nut-free – sold as a Bar or as Lollies

Lidl Fair Trade Dark: good value, good quality

Montezuma: several types and shapes of dark chocolate

Moo Free: vegan rice milk chocolate in various flavours and shapes (bars, drops – and Christmas products!)

Organica: Couverture Bar (milk-style, a bit like a vegan Galaxy); White Bar – white vegan chocolate

Plamil: a dedicated vegan company which sells a wide range of quality chocolate from milky to 70% dark. They also do organic, sugar-free and carob bars

Sainsbury's: Crispy Rice Choc Bar

Tesco: Free-from Chocolate Bar

Waitrose: Belgian Dark – on its own or with nuts or fruit and nut

Viva!

Alternatives to Mars, Snickers, Milky Way and Bounty are available from
www.vivashop.org.uk/catalog/viva/food/chocolates

Chocolate know-how

- Dark (or plain) chocolate is sometimes but not always vegan. Sometimes companies add whey, butter fat or other bits of dairy (why?!)
- Some supermarket own-brand dark chocolate is suitable when you look at the ingredients list
- A dark chocolate label might state 'may contain traces of milk' in the packaging information because it's made in a factory with mixed production lines – even though the ingredients are vegan. See page 14 for the allergen vs vegan explanation!

Confectionery

Biona: Cola Bottles; Wine Gums; Pineapple Chews
Goody Goody Stuff: Cola Breeze; Summer Peaches; Sour Mix & Match; Sour Fruit Salad. Available from Asda and Viva!
Holy Cow Dairy-free Fudge: available from VeggieStuff
Just Wholefoods: Veggiebear range
M&S: Flying Saucers; Menthol Eucalyptus Gum; Peppermint Gum; Rhubarb & Custards; Sugar Free Mints; Sugar Free Orange & Lemon Fruit Drops
Fabulous Fudge Factory Dairy-free Fudge: available from Redwood and Viva!
Sainsbury's: Fruit Jellies; Fizzy Fangs; Fizzy Strawberry Lances; Strawberry Pencils; Mint imperials; Flying saucers; Basics Sherbet cocktails; Turkish Delight

There are lots more vegan sweets available online – see page 38 – and check supermarket vegan lists also

Desserts, chilled
Waitrose: Summer Pudding
See individual supermarket lists also

Desserts, frozen
Food Heaven: Cheesecake (assorted flavours) and Tiramisu from selected branches of Tesco and Waitrose
Mama Cucina: Cheesecake (assorted flavours) from H&B; Goodness Direct etc
Sainsbury's: Woodland Fruit Strudel
Tesco: Value Apple Pie; Strudel – Apple or Woodland Fruit

Ice cream and similar
Bessant & Dury: assorted flavours, delicious. The lemon is particularly good
Booja Booja: pure, nut-based, pricey but very good. The Pompompous Maple Pecan is a particular favourite
Swedish Glace: a range of flavours. Most large supermarkets sell the vanilla; Waitrose and H&B sell the other flavours
Tofutti: ice cream and cones
Sorbet: many brands, almost all vegan and widely available. See individual supermarket sections

Desserts, long-life
Alpro and Provamel: soya desserts, assorted flavours
Co-op: Rich Fruit Christmas Pudding; Truly Irresistible Christmas Pudding
Granovita: Jellovita
Fruit pieces in Jelly: see Sainsbury's (page 28), M&S (page 22) and Waitrose (page 33) or their vegan lists. Not all jelly is vegan – check the label to make sure there is no gelatine used

Sugar and other sweeteners

Vegans don't eat honey but there are plenty of sweet
alternatives. We list the most available brands but there are
others out there too, especially syrups.

Agave Syrup:
Biona Organic (light and dark varieties)
Crazy Jack
Hale & Hearty

Barley Malt Syrup:
Clearspring
Meridian

Brown Rice Syrup:
Biona
Clearspring
Crazy Jack
Now

Date Syrup:
Meridian
Or try a good deli that sells original Middle Eastern date syrup
such as Basra brand.

Golden Syrup:
Tate & Lyle
Supermarket own-brands are usually vegan, but check.

Maple Syrup:
Meridian
Sainsbury's: Pure Canadian Maple Syrup

Molasses (black treacle):
A fantastic source of iron!
Meridian

Other:
Sweetbird

Sugar

Billington: all their range is vegan. However, Golden Icing Sugar is 'made in a factory which uses eggs' but that doesn't mean egg is added to the sugar. See page 14

Co-op: Fairtrade Dark Brown Soft; Fairtrade Demerara; Fairtrade Golden Granulated; Fairtrade Light Brown Soft; Fairtrade White Granulated

Silver Spoon: all sugar and sweetener products are suitable (NOT Royal Icing sugar)

Tate & Lyle: all their sugar and syrup range (NOT Royal Icing)

Waitrose: Dark Brown Soft; Light Brown Soft; Golden Granulated; Golden Caster; Demerara; Light Muscovado; Dark Muscovado; Fair Trade Granulated Cane; A Sprinkle of Cinnamon Sugar; A Sprinkle of Lavender Sugar

Viva!

Toiletries, cosmetics, medicines & vitamins

These companies sell all or mostly vegan products, but check their websites. As ever, this isn't a fully comprehensive list but there is more than enough to get you started!

Always check with each manufacturer to check they haven't changed the 'recipe'! And remember, certain drug companies may be less than ethical when it comes to animal testing so do your homework. BUAV www.buav.org.

Many **medicines** contain gelatine or other animal ingredients. Ask your GP for an alternative prescription – or the pharmacist if you are buying over the counter products. **Vitamins** may also be non-vegan although there are plenty of brands that are OK, eg Solgar – check the label and ask the shop assistant. See also page 90 for information on vitamin D – and brands.

A close shave?

Many razor blades aren't vegan – animal products are used in the strip – but some are OK

Preserve: Viva! Shop and elsewhere

Superdrug: own brands

BIC: all vegan EXCEPT for these:

Soleil Twilight
Soleil Twist (MvB)
Savvy
Simply Soleil/Miss Soleil
Soleil Shave and Trim
Comfort Twin Lady
Comfort Teens Purple
Comfort 2
Action Blue
Action Black
Action Green
Flex O3
Action Pink
Comfort Teens Green

Barry M Cosmetics: see page 36
Beaming Baby
Beauty Without Cruelty: cosmetics – the original vegan make-up company!
Bohemian Chic Minerals: cosmetics
Co-op: some of their range – toothpaste, roll-on deodorant, some shampoos and conditioners etc
Emotional Brilliance: all vegan cosmetic range from Lush
Faith in Nature: everything in range is vegan except for Neem and Propolis hair care products
GOSH Cosmetics: see page 37
Green People: have a separate vegan range
Hard Candy: cosmetics. Some of their range is vegan, available at www.hardcandy.com and other online stores
Honesty Cosmetics: all vegan company. They have their own range and also sell many other vegan products on their website www.honestycosmetics.co.uk
Incognito: eg Insect Repellent
Lavera: cosmetics as well as skin, hair etc. Lots of their products are vegan – for further information check out www.lavera.com/blog/which-lavera-products-are-certified-vegan
Lush: look for the Vegan Society symbol on products or ask the helpful staff
Skin Blossom: all vegan and registered organic skin and hair care
Suncoat: nail polish, mascara; liquid foundations are vegan but check – not everything they sell is vegan (eg lip glosses and lipsticks)
Superdrug: see pages 35-37
Urban Decay: some of their range is vegan and BUAV approved. www.urbandecay.com – go to 'Shop' then 'Vegan' for several pages of cool products!

Viva!

Contraceptives
Condoms
Many are not vegan because latex often contains casein, a milk by-product.

Viva! Shop sells condoms **www.vivashop.org.uk/viva/viva-valentines/fusion-condoms** or try these:

NVS Ltd: all
Boots: own brand, all
Condomi: all
Durex: Avanti; Real Feel; Fetherlite Ultra and Deluxe (all non-latex)
Glyde Health: Latex Condoms; Sheer Glyde Dams
Lifestyles: all
Mates: Mates SKYN
ONE: all except ONE Zero
Pasante: all latex condoms
Safex: all
Sir Richard's Condom Company: all
Tesco: all Sequre range

Oral Contraceptives
Pfizer: Femulen

Contraceptive Patches
Janssen-Cilag: Evra

Contraceptive Injection
Bayer: Noristerat
Pfizer: Depo-Provera

Feminine Hygiene
Mooncup: alternative to tampons and towels. Available from health food shops – high street and online; Boots; Amazon etc

Natracare: tampons and towels. Available from health food shops – high street and online. Also Waitrose and Ocado

Household cleaning products
Astonish: www.astonishcleaners.com/where/find.php
Bio-D: all
Co-op: some of their range, eg dishwasher tablets, laundry. All suitable products are clearly labelled as free from animal products and testing
Earth Friendly
Ecoleaf
Ecozone
Faith in Nature
Method

Useful sites
- BUAV www.buav.org supply a list of approved companies that are both vegan and non-tested for further information E: info@buav.org T: 020 7700 4888
- www.thebeautydiaries.net/p/cruelty-free-ranges.html

Candles
Vegan-friendly candles are made from plant oils like soya – longer burning and better for the environment – or paraffin. These can be found in mainstream outlets but always read the label/ask an assistant.

Non-vegan candles use animal fats (tallow, stearin etc) or beeswax.

A Lot of Candles: all vegan range of candles and more **www.alotofcandles.co.uk**
Aroma Candles: soya candles
Brackencraft: a dedicated vegan company
Heaven Scent: lovely tealights!
IKEA: quite a lot of their range is clearly marked as made from plant sources – others, especially the long thin type, are labelled as made with stearin so are not vegan or vegetarian

Clothing and shoes

Clothing might seem easy and mostly it is. With a vast array of ethical fibres such as bamboo, hemp and organic cotton, quality modern synthetics and amazing fake furs – there is plenty to choose from! However, vegans avoid wool, silk, fur, leather and feathers, all of which come from a living or dead animal – sadly, cruelty and exploitation are embedded in these industries.

Shoes

Obviously, vegans don't use leather or suede. However, there are decisions for new vegans – for financial and ecological reasons you may want to wear out leather footwear before buying vegan versions. Just be honest – if someone quizzes you about it, explain why!

Many vegan online stores sell a variety of brands. We even found vegan footwear on Amazon but do check the product matches the search!

Many high street stores, including big supermarket chains, often sell non-leather shoes although the glues may be of animal origin – you will need to check with the company. Try Shoe Zone; George at Asda; New Look and others.

Beyond Skin: designer shoes **www.beyondskin.co.uk**
Bourgeois Boheme: contemporary footwear and accessories
www.bboheme.com
Eco Vegan Shoes: **www.eco-vegan-shoes.com**
Marco Tozzi: a lot of their range is vegan. Mastershoe/MyShu stocks them, as do some vegan companies, and the glues are animal-free
Vegetarian Shoes: (Brighton shop and online)
www.vegetarian-shoes.co.uk

The Airseal PARA BOOT

VEGETARIAN SHOES®

ANIMAL FRIENDLY FOOTWEAR

100+ mens & womens styles: Casual, Formal, Sport, Leisure, Work, Hiking, Dress, Fashion, Sandals, Belts & Accessories.

Made in England & Europe with quality 'breathable' non-leather materials.

Est. 1990

Available in **8** mouthwatering colours...
BLACK | BLUE | GREEN | PURPLE | RED | PINK | SKY BLUE | WHITE

ORDER DIRECT AT: **www.vegshoes.com** Tel: **01273 691913** info@vegshoes.com

A TREAT FOR YOUR FEET
IF YOU DON'T EAT MEAT!

Viva!

Trainers

Many trainers are inherently vegan but the glues might be an issue (as might be their employment policies!). Asics have a vegan list – contact them for more info. Most of the other big companies sell vegan trainers – again, check. New Balance and Brooks are particularly good.

Walking boots

As well as the dedicated vegan companies who sell walking boots such as Vegetarian Shoes (see page 76), many of the big companies offer at least one vegan boot in their range, eg Salomon; Karrimor; Aku La Stria.

The animal skin on the left means that leather/suede has been used. The other two symbols mean fabric and 'other materials', respectively.

Booze

Beer

Many cans and bottled beers are fine yet their cask equivalents may not be. This isn't a comprehensive list but you will find at least one of these in your local.

Becks: all
Budweiser: all
Carlsberg: regular; Edge; Export; Special Brew
Cobra: all
Coors: all
Corona: all
Co-op: own-label beers clearly marked on the label if vegan, eg Czech lager

For a complete list of vegan booze, check **www.barnivore.com** or 'The Animal-free Shopper' guide – and if you find a new vegan booze product, please contact them.

Why would booze not be vegan?! Well, it all depends on what the manufacturer uses to fine (clarify) a product. Beware:

- albumen (egg)
- casein (milk protein)
- gelatine (animal bones)
- isinglass (fish bladder)

Does organic mean it is vegan? No! The grapes/hops/apples etc might be OK but that doesn't mean the fining agent is animal-free.

Bentonite is vegan – it's a mineral. Some manufacturers don't fine their wines at all, making life easier!

Viva!

Deuchars: Bottled
Elephant: Bottled
Freedom: Lager, Bottled
Golden Promise: Bottled
Grolsch: all
Heineken: Pilsner
Holsten: Export; Pils; Super
M&S: their vegan list includes lots of vegan booze, not just wine
Perroni Nastro Azzurro: Bottled
Samuel Smith:
- Bottles: all vegan EXCEPT Yorkshire Stingo
- Cask: all EXCEPT Old Brewery Bitter hand pulled from the cask – this is fined with traditional isinglass

San Miguel: bottled
Tiger: Bottled
Tsingtao: Bottled
Tuborg: all
Tyskie: all

Cider
Aspall: all
Dunkertons: all
Luscombe Organic: all
Merrydown: all
Samuel Smith: Cider Reserve; Organic Cider
Sheppy's Cider: all
Stowford Press: all
Thatcher's: all
Weston & Son: all

Fortified wines – sherry and port
Cockburns: Vintage Port; Quintas dos Canais Vintage Port
Fonseca: Forty Year Old Aged Tawny Port; Quinta do Panescal Single Quinta Vintage Port; Classic Vintage Port; Guimaraens

Vintage Port; Late Bottled Vintage Port
Harvey's Bristol Cream
Waitrose: Waitrose Amontillado; Waitrose Fino only

Spirits
Most spirits are vegan but not advocaat, which contains eggs

Wine
Viva! Wine Club can supply most of your alcohol needs – not just
wine – delivered straight to your door!
www.viva.org.uk/wineshop

Asda: marks its own-label wines.
Brown Brothers: it varies!
www.brownbrothers.com.au/uploads/veganapril2011.pdf –
contact them for a more current list
Co-op: see Co-op beer and cider
Majestic: has a vegan list www.majestic.co.uk/find/Vegan-is-Vegan
M&S: marks its own wines if suitable. See M&S beer and cider
Oxford Landing: all of its range from 2008 vintage onwards is vegan
Sainsbury's: marks its own-label wines
Tesco: as Sainsbury's. However, their wine website only lists four
vegan wines but they actually sell many more. Read the labels
and ask customer services. And keep phoning/emailing until they
give in and update their website!
Waitrose: www.waitrosedirect.com/wine/vegetarian/1
Yellow Tail: all red (the white uses gelatine)
www.discoveryellowtail.com
Independents: most independents know their stuff and should
be able to tell you what is suitable

Eating out
Chains and independents

These all have an allergy list and some vegan options:

- Las Iguanas
- Nandos
- Pizza Express
- Pizza Hut
- Prezzo
- Wagamama
- Wetherspoon
- Yo Sushi

In addition, all chains now offer a list of allergy-free foods in their range. This doesn't guarantee that there will be much for vegans but it's a start. For more detailed info, check out **www.cookingforvegans.co.uk/eatingout/chainrestaurantinfo.html**

Independents vary massively regarding how vegan-friendly they are. This includes pubs as well as dedicated restaurants and cafés. Always check their website and phone beforehand; give at least 24 hours' notice if possible – even if they don't have anything on the menu they may be able to whip something up if you ask nicely. Indeed, sometimes you get the best food off-menu! If you want to encourage a business refer them to the Vegan Catering Guide **www.veganrecipeclub.org.uk/catering**

On the move
Motorway

The best services are **Moto** – these contain a M&S Simply Food and Costa Coffee (soya milk for hot drinks). Other than baked potato, beans and chips, main meals may be a bit random although it is always worth asking. M&S multi salads are a great standby if choice is lacking!

Little Chef: good for a vegan breakfast (hash browns, cooked tomatoes, baked beans, toast [avoid the butter and marg] etc). At time of writing they don't supply soya milk but are looking into

Viva!

it. If you have time, phone and politely ask them to stock it. T: 01953 450053

Bus and railway stations
No vegan food on trains or coaches as yet – other than crisps! – but some chains within the station itself may offer food and many have soya milk for hot drinks. When in doubt bring your own or pick up provisions from a nearby chain such as H&B, M&S, WHSmith, Pret a Manger, Starbucks…

Airlines
The rule of three is useful to ensure you get a decent meal.
1. Ask for a vegan meal when you book a flight. All airlines do them, though quality varies. Ask for soya milk also, particularly if on a long-haul flight.
2. Phone again to check a couple of days before departure.
3. Ask again when you check in.

Airports
Starbucks or other chains may provide vegan food but check on the airport's website to see which food outlets are there. When in doubt, stock up with portable snacks, such as fruit, nuts, seeds and sandwiches. You may not be allowed to take food on board the plane with you however, particularly if travelling out of Europe.

More ideas
www.cookingforvegans.co.uk/eatingout/foodonthego.html
www.veganbackpacker.com/featured-articles/vegan-vegetarian-travel-tips
www.happycow.net – global website for vegans and veggies. Includes health food shops as well as places to eat
www.vegdining.com – global site
www.vegetarianvisitor.co.uk – UK site
And there are plenty more!

Health matters

A balanced vegan diet is the healthiest diet on earth, and yet some people still have a few concerns about whether they will receive all the nutrients that they require. Let us put your mind at rest!

For further information Viva! Guide 1 – Nutrition in a Nutshell.
www.vegetarian.org.uk/guides/Nutrition-in-a-Nutshell.pdf

This handy guide also features two simple charts: Nutrition and Daily Healthy Eating.

Nutritional basics
Calcium

It isn't necessary to eat animal products like dairy for calcium – after all, over 70 per cent of the world's population does not eat it traditionally because they are lactose intolerant. Moreover, such people tend to have lower rates of osteoporosis than Westerners. They get their calcium from other sources – plants.

Calcium is found in:
- green leafy veg such as kale, cabbage, spinach, fennel, watercress, leeks and broccoli. One serving of broccoli contains as much calcium as 200ml of cows' milk
- pulses (peas, beans, lentils)
- nuts, especially almonds and Brazil nuts – and seeds, especially sesame (including hummus and tahini – sesame paste)
- figs and olives
- sea vegetables such as arame – delicious in a brown rice and carrot salad
- fortified soya and almond milks (contain very similar amounts as cows' milk)
- cinnamon

Viva!

Although we do need calcium for our bones, we can lose it through our urine. People who eat a typical Western diet – that is, one based on animal protein (including cow's milk) are likely to lose more calcium, and are therefore more at risk of osteoporosis than those who only eat vegetable proteins. This is partly because animal protein leaches calcium out of the bones, whereas vegetable protein does not. The Innuit people – whose diet is based almost entirely on meat – have the highest osteoporosis rates in the world.

But isn't milk natural? No! It is completely unnatural to drink milk after weaning. And bizarre to drink the milk of another species. Cows' milk is meant for calves; goats' milk for kids and sheeps' milk for lambs!

So, you see, the vegan diet really is the healthiest option! There is little chance of a deficiency of calcium, or any other food group, vitamin or mineral, as long as you eat a balanced diet.

For further information see our calcium fact sheet
www.vegetarian.org.uk/campaigns/bones/factsheet.html

Iron and vitamin C
According to the British Medical Association, iron deficiency can be a problem that affects everyone, whatever their diet – and particularly women. Vegans are no more likely to be iron deficient than anyone else – but it is something that we all need to take care with. Increase your intake of iron and vitamin C-rich foods and, if necessary, take a plant-based supplement such as Floradix.

Iron is found in:
- green leafy vegetables: green cabbage, curly kale, cavalo nero, Brussels sprouts, spinach, chard etc
- wholegrains such as wholemeal bread, brown rice and wholegrain pasta
- dried fruit

- pulses: beans, lentils, peas – and tofu, which is made from soya beans
- black treacle (molasses)
- many fortified breakfast cereals
- cocoa and plain chocolate!

Eating vitamin C-rich foods helps iron absorption by three to four times! Here are some good combinations:

- baked beans on wholemeal toast with grilled tomatoes or tomato salad
- broccoli with a serving of freshly squeezed orange juice
- stir-fried tofu with broccoli
- curly kale (high in both iron and vitamin C) stir-fried with fresh thyme and chopped chillies
- soya milk shake with blueberries and dried dates or figs

It's not difficult, as vegans tend to eat lots more vitamin C-rich fruit and veg with their food anyway! For example:

- green leafy veg
- broccoli
- parsley
- frozen peas
- green peppers
- potatoes
- tomatoes
- citrus fruits
- mangoes
- blackcurrants

For further information
see our iron fact sheet
www.vegetarian.org.uk/factsheets/iron.html

Viva!

Protein

Protein is essential for growth, repairing tissues and protecting against infections. The British Medical Association states that the vegan diet provides all nutrient requirements, including more than enough protein. According to leading nutritionists, it really is very difficult to suffer from protein deficiency unless you go out of your way to do so – ie starve!

Protein can be found in:

- pulses: peas, beans of all types, lentils (whole and split) and soya products, eg soya milk, soya burgers, tofu and tempeh
- wholegrains: rice, quinoa, millet, wheat, bulghur, couscous, oats, barley, buckwheat, pasta, bread
- nuts and nut butters: Brazils, hazels, walnuts, pine nuts, macadamia nuts, pecans, almonds, peanuts etc
- seeds and seed butters: hemp, sunflower, pumpkin, sesame etc (tahini paste – used in hummus – is made from sesame)

Vitamin B12

We used to get our B12 naturally from the microorganisms in soil on fruit and vegetables but modern farming methods have put an end to that. Interestingly, gorillas – who are vegan – naturally get enough B12 in the wild but those imprisoned in zoos have to be given a supplement.

The human body only needs a tiny amount of vitamin B12 per day (and B12 deficiency is relatively rare in the young) but it is important to get a daily dose of it because it

- maintains a healthy nervous system
- aids normal blood formation
- keeps the heart in tip top condition

Vitamin B12 is found in many everyday foods that have been fortified with it such as yeast extracts (eg Marmite or Merdian Yeast Extract with B12), many breakfast cereals, yeast-based spreads and pâtés, soya milk and soya margarines. Foods containing soya protein are also fortified with this vitamin such as TVP (textured vegetable protein), soya sausages and soya burgers.

While the daily requirement is only 1.5 micrograms, some experts now believe that 3 micrograms per day is a more healthy intake – and according to the National Academy of Sciences in the US, all adults over 50 – whatever their diet – should take a supplement or eat fortified foods.

In summary:
- Take a supplement
- OR eat these foods regularly
  - 250ml serving of fortified soya milk
  - 50g serving of fortified cereal
  - Two pieces of toast with a spread of B12 fortified margarine and B12 fortified yeast extract

Viva!

Vitamin D

The best source is sunlight on bare skin, but many of us in the UK – whatever our diet – miss out in the winter months. Most vitamin D in fortified foods (eg breakfast cereal; margarine) is not vegan. However, most fortified plant milks use a vegan source of the vitamin.

Vitamin D2 (always vegan) supplements are available from **www.veganicity.com/Vitamin-D.html**. Vegan vitamin D3 is available from **www.vitashine-d3.com**

For further information about nutrition, see Viva! Health **www.vivahealth.org.uk** for a wide range of science-based guides, nutritional fact sheets and scientific reports, including the *Vegetarian and Vegan Mother and Baby Guide* for pregnancy and baby nutrition and *Food of Champions* for sports nutrition.

Get yourself a full list of all the Guides available from: Viva! Health, 8 York Court, Wilder Street, Bristol BS2 8QH. E: info@viva.org.uk T: 0117 944 1000. Alternatively, you can view all our nutritional guides and plenty more veggie info FREE at **www.viva.org.uk** and **www.vivahealth.org.uk**.

New ingredients list

Some of these products may be new to you – or they may be given a different name if you use recipes from the USA or Canada.

Agar flakes/powder: thickening agent derived from seaweed. (Also called agar agar). See also **Gelatine, Vegetarian** and **Vegegel**

Alfalfa sprouts: comes in different varieties also. Delicate sprouted seeds, full of vitamins and goodness – available from health food shops. Or grow your own! See www.veganrecipeclub.org.uk/super-sprouts

Arrowroot: a bit like cornflour, a good sauce and gravy thickener but it doesn't change the colour of the sauce in the way cornflour does. Cheapest bought from a good health food shop, otherwise Tesco or Waitrose offer the best own-brand deals

Arugala: (used in USA and Canada) rocket

Bulgur: cracked wheat

Celeriac: the root of celery; eat it grated in salads, or boil/bake it

Couscous: tiny pieces of semolina used in Middle Eastern and North African cooking. Good and quick as the basis for a salad – similar to bulgur

Earth Balance: a US vegan margarine. UK versions include Biona, Pure or Suma. See page 55

Eggplant: (used in USA and Canada) aubergine

Flax: omega-rich seeds. Grind them up to get your omega-3 and 9. See also linseed

Gelatine, vegetarian: as opposed to the animal version! A setting agent used to make jellies etc. It is available from various outlets. See also agar and Vegegel

Hemp: a protein and omega-rich seed. The hemp plant is also used to make an ecological alternative to cotton

Humous/hummus: a dip made from chickpeas, tahini and garlic

Kohlrabi: a type of turnip

Linseed: omega-rich seeds. See **Flax**. Ground seeds can also be mixed with a little water and used as an egg-replacer in baking

Mange-tout: also called snow peas, lovely raw or cooked

Millet: tiny bright yellow wholegrains, use instead of rice

Miso: mineral-rich paste made from fermented soya beans – used as a stock for soups and stews. It comes in different strengths – pale and slightly sweet to dark brown and more 'meaty' in flavour

Nori: a sea vegetable used for wrapping sushi. Nori sprinkles are also used as a condiment and are rich in vitamins and minerals

Nutritional yeast flakes: a tasty, nutty, slightly cheesy condiment full of B vitamins – used to make sauces or just added to soup, pasta dishes etc. Engevita brand is sold in health food shops in the high street and online. Not to be confused with brewers' yeast

Quinoa: (pronounced 'keenwah') – a small, nutty-tasting, protein-packed wholegrain

Rutabaga: swede (US and Canada)

Seitan: also known as gluten, it is a wheat-based meat replacement. See page 44

Shoyu: see **Soya sauce** and **Tamari**

Soya sauce: the best is shoyu or tamari (which is wheat-free). Brands include Essential, Clearspring and Sanchi and are widely available. It is made using traditional methods and tastes far better than the usual type. Fantastic in stir-fries, sauces etc

Tahini: ground sesame paste, used as a spread or to thicken sauces. Also used in hummus

Tamari: see **Shoyu** and **Soya sauce**

Tempeh: protein-rich soya bean product; has a nutty taste. See page 44-45

Tofu: soya bean curd. See page 45-46

TVP: textured vegetable protein, made from soya, comes in mince and chunks. See page 40-41

Vegegel: a brand of vegetarian/vegan setting agent. See also **Agar** and **Gelatine, vegetarian**

Yeast extract: eg Marmite, Natex, Vegemite, Essential, Meridian brands. Each has a slightly different flavour and salt percentage. Use as a spread or to flavour soups and stews

Zucchini: (used in USA and Canada) courgettes. From the marrow family, use this veg raw or cooked

Viva!

Hidden nasties – things to avoid

Albumen: egg white, used in food as a binder (sadly, some vegetarian sausages and burgers contain this, eg Cauldron brand)
Anchovy: small fish, often used in Worcester sauce
Angora: a type of wool made from goat or rabbit hair
Aspic: meat or fish-derived jelly
Beeswax (E901): secreted by bees, used in polishes and cosmetics
Beta carotene: is vegan but may be bound to gelatine and may not be listed in the ingredients
Bristle: animal hair used for brushes
Carmine: red pigment obtained from cochineal
Casein: milk-derived protein
Cashmere: wool from the cashmere goat
Caviar: see roe
Chitin: derived from the shells of insects or crustacea, used in shampoos and moisturisers
Chamois: soft leather, made from the skin of antelope, sheep, goat or deer
Cochineal (E120): red dye made from the dried bodies of insects
Collagen: constituent of connective tissue, used in cosmetics
Vitamin D3: vitamin derived from lanolin or fish oil. Added to vitamin and food supplements
Down: feathers from fowl, used in quilts and pillows (duck, geese and chicken feathers are either a slaughterhouse by-product – or else are plucked cruelly from live birds)
Elastin: protein found in the muscles of meat, used in cosmetics
Felt: cloth made from wool and fur
Glycerin(e) or **glycerol** (E422): colourless liquid which can be obtained from animal fats
Hide: animal skin used in clothing, footwear and upholstery

L-Plate Vegan

Honey: some bees are inevitably injured or killed when the combs are removed. And it is their food, not ours

Isinglass: pure form of gelatine, obtained from freshwater fish

Keratin: protein found in hair, horns, hoofs and feathers, used in shampoos and conditioners

L-cysteine hydrochloride (E920): obtained from animal hair or chicken feathers, used in shampoos and as an improving agent in white flour. Can be produced synthetically

Lactic acid (E270): acid produced by fermenting milk sugar. Can also be obtained from non-dairy source – eg Patak's curry pastes use a vegan version. Check with the company

Lactose: milk sugar, often found in crisps

Lanolin(e): fat extracted from sheeps' wool, used in cosmetics

Lard: fat surrounding stomach and kidneys in sheep

Leather: tanned hide (animal skin), used in clothing, accessories and upholstery

Lecithin (E322): fatty substance found in nerve tissues, egg yolk and blood. Can also be obtained from vegetable sources

Lutein (E161(b)): dye obtained from egg yolk. May also be obtained from marigolds

Mohair: cloth made from hair of angora goat

Oleic acid: fatty acid found in animal and vegetable fats

Oestrogen: female sex hormone, used in cosmetics and body-building supplements

Parchment: skin of sheep or goat, used as a writing material

Pepsin: enzyme found in stomach gastric juices, used in cheese-making

Progesterone: sex hormone used in hormone creams

Propolis: bee glue, used in toiletries and cosmetics

Rennet: extract of calf stomach, used in cheese-making

Roe: eggs obtained from slaughtered female fish

Royal jelly: food upon which bee larvae are fed, used as a food supplement

Sable: fur from small mammal, the sable marten, used in artists'

and make-up brushes etc

Shellac (E904): insect secretion, used in hair spray, lip sealer and polishes

Silk: fibre produced by larvae of certain bombycine moths, who are killed

Sodium 5'-inosinate: prepared from fish waste, used as a flavour enhancer

Squalene/squalane: found in the liver of sharks, used in toiletries and cosmetics

Stearin(e): general term for glycerids formed by combining stearic acid and glycerin. Used in some candles, medicines and toiletries

Suede: kid, pig or calf skin, made into clothes and footwear

Suet: fat prepared from the kidneys of cattle and sheep (vegetarian suet is acceptable)

Tallow: hard animal fat, often obtained from around the kidneys of cattle, used in soap and candle-making

Taramasalata: cod roe pâté (eggs from killed cod)

Testosterone: male hormone, used in body-building supplements

Urea: waste nitrogen formed in the liver, used in toiletries and cosmetics

Velvet: fabric usually made from silk, but can also be made synthetically

Whey: milk derivative. Used in margarines, biscuits, crisps and cleaning products

Wool: fleece of sheep. See page 7

For a more detailed list, see
www.vivahealth.org.uk/factsheets/hiddennasties.html